GEOMETRY

AN INTRODUCTION

H. G. FORDER

PROFESSOR EMERITUS,
UNIVERSITY OF AUCKLAND,
NEW ZEALAND

GEOMETRY

HARPER TORCHBOOKS

THE SCIENCE LIBRARY

HARPER & BROTHERS, NEW YORK

GEOMETRY

PRINTED IN THE UNITED STATES OF AMERICA

This book was first published in 1950, with a revised edition in 1960, in the Mathematics division, edited by Dr. F. C. Powell, of the Hutchinson University Library. It is reprinted by arrangement with Hutchinson & Company Limited, London.

First HARPER TORCHBOOK edition published 1962

CONTENTS

	Preface	7
I	Euclidean Geometry	9
II	An Introduction to Plane Curves	30
III	Co-ordinate Geometry	38
IV	Projective Geometry	56
V	Non-Euclidean Geometry	80
VI	The Logical Structure of Geometries	96
VII	Solid Geometry	114
VIII	Differential Geometry in Space	131
IX	Algebraic Plane Curves	150
X	Many Dimensions and Representational Geometry	167
XI	General Space	179
	References	193
	Index	195

The following is a shortened course of reading.
We give the numbers of the chapters and sections.

I.   1–20, 24, 25.   II.   III.   36–45.

IV.   61–72, 75–83, 86.   V.   94–102, 109.

VI.   110–118, 124–126.   VII.   131–139, 141, 142.

VIII.   153–158, 160, 161.   IX.   165–168, 176, 177.

PREFACE

GEOMETRY, the oldest of the Sciences, is still developing after more than two thousand years of life. I have tried to give an introduction, from a modern point of view, to its main branches, apart from topology, and it is hoped that the greater part of most chapters will be readily understood.

If towards the end of any chapter, the reader finds it too strenuous, he should turn to the next for a fresh beginning.

Too great generality leads to haziness: a catalogue of special theorems would read like a dictionary: my chief anxiety has been to avoid these two pit-falls.

The stress on axioms and the logical connection of theorems is a feature of this century's thought, but I have maintained a balance between this and the picturesque intuitive treatment which must always have its proper place.

In most of the book, only a little algebra is assumed, and in some chapters an acquaintance with differentiation. The last three chapters are more severe, but it is hoped that, even there, the general trend can be followed if the details have to be taken as read.

If the meaning of some technical term is not remembered by the reader, the index will tell him where to find its definition.

With much regret I have excluded all reference to the applications, which I greatly prize, of the "Calculus of Extension" to geometry. I had the choice of dealing with these inadequately or of writing the whole book from that point of view, and neither course seemed desirable.

To my colleague Mr. C. M. Segedin, my thanks are due for criticisms which led to the removal of many ambiguities and obscurities. To Mr. P. W. Taylor I am indebted for most of the figures which presented any difficulty. The figure of Steiner's ring (p. 23) was drawn for me by Mr. J. H. Clarke, and, in my absence from England, the figures were corrected for printing by Prof. E. A. Milne. The reader of this book will not need to be told how much I owe to these helpers.

Auckland, New Zealand   H.G.F.
Nottingham, England

Preface to Second Edition

In this edition some corrections and additions have been made. My thanks are due to Editorial Novaro of Mexico for the honour they have done me in publishing a Spanish translation of this book.

Auckland   H.G.F.
1959

CHAPTER I

EUCLIDEAN GEOMETRY

MOST readers of this book will have studied elementary geometry at some time of their lives, but the outlook in this chapter may nevertheless be new to them; it is easily understood in this elementary case and is fundamental in much more difficult work. And as geometry contains not only theories but also striking theorems, and as later ones are more easily grasped when earlier ones have been appreciated, we shall refresh the reader's memory by mentioning and sketching the proofs of certain theorems in elementary geometry. Those who already know them as old friends may see them with new faces.

1. Euclidean geometry deals with the notions of congruence and similarity; the first occurs in other geometries also, but the second is peculiar to Euclidean geometry.

Two figures, whether made up of points and curves in a plane, or of points, surfaces and solids in space, are called "congruent" when they have the same size and shape, and "similar" when they agree in shape but not necessarily in size. Thus two spheres with equal radii are congruent, and, if we ignored the impenetrability of matter, we could *move* one of them until it coincided with the other.

It is of such *motions* we shall first speak, and although the idea, like all geometrical ideas, is drawn from experience, we shall, in the end, view it abstractly. It is then a particular *transformation* which turns one figure into another, the intermediate steps being disregarded.

2. *Reflections.* To begin with, we take a particular transformation in a plane which turns points into points, namely, a *reflection in a line.* If OA is a fixed line, we reflect a point P in it when we draw the perpendicular from P to the line and continue it to a point Q at the same distance on the other side of the line. We have merely the looking-glass reflection, and we say P, Q are "images" of each other. When P describes

a figure, Q describes the image figure; we have a "transformation" of figures, and it is *"indirect"*, that is, it reverses the sense (or direction) in which figures are described.

Suppose a second reflection in another line OB be made after the first, and suppose this turns Q into R; since each reflection reverses the sense in which figures are described, the combination preserves the sense; it is a *"direct"* transformation. A combination of two or more transformations is usually called their *"product"*. To find the nature of the product of two reflections, we observe that $OP = OR$, since each equals OQ, and that $\measuredangle\ POR$ is twice $\measuredangle\ AOB$, since

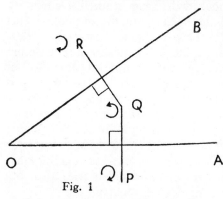

Fig. 1

$\measuredangle\ POA = \measuredangle\ AOQ$ and $\measuredangle\ QOB = \measuredangle\ BOR$. Thus if by the product of these reflections, P becomes R, then $OP = OR$, and the angle POR does not depend on the position of P. Thus the transformation, being direct, is a *rotation round O* through twice the angle AOB. Incidentally we note that the right bisectors of the sides of triangle PQR meet in the point O.

The reader will easily find that the product of reflections in two parallel lines is a *translation*, in a direction perpendicular to the lines, through twice the distance between them, where by a translation in a plane we mean a transformation which turns any point P into Q, such that the interval PQ has a fixed direction and length.

3. Conversely, any rotation round a point O can be resolved into successive reflections in two lines through O, and as the only condition on these lines is that the angle between them is half the angle of the rotation, we can choose any line through O for the first or for the second of the lines in which the reflection is made; the other is then definite.

Similarly any translation can be resolved into successive reflections in any two lines of the set perpendicular to the direction of translation, and of these two, either the first or the second can be chosen arbitrarily from this set.

Simple as these results are, we shall find they are typical of more difficult ones.

4. *Displacements.* Now consider any displacement in a plane. A figure (think of a polygon) is shifted in the plane from one position to another; we consider only the initial and final positions.

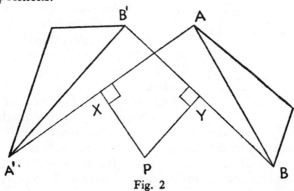

Fig. 2

Suppose A, B, points of the figure in its first position become A', B' in its final position. Join AA', BB' and let their right bisectors PX, PY meet in P. Then it is easy to see that the triangles PAB, $PA'B'$ are congruent, and hence that the displacement of the whole figure is a rotation round P.

If the right bisectors were parallel, then AA', BB' would be parallel, and the displacement would be a translation.

It is often better to think not of the displacement of a polygon from one position to another, but of the displacement of the whole plane; we imagine a fixed plane like a table and another plane like a large sheet of paper on it; the paper is moved with all the figures on it, from one position over the table to another.

Thus *every displacement in a plane is either a translation or a rotation, and hence is the product of reflections in two lines.*

5. What happens when we displace a figure in a plane and then perform a second displacement? What, in other words, is the product of two displacements?

Take two rotations, one round A of angle α, followed by one round B of angle β. The first is the product of reflections in two lines through A, inclined at an angle $\frac{1}{2}\alpha$, and either the first or the second can be any line through A. Take the line AB for the second, and call the first AX. The rotation round

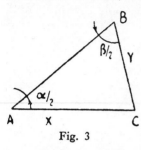

Fig. 3

B is the product of reflections in two lines through B inclined at an angle $\frac{1}{2}\beta$, and of these we take BA for the first, and call the second BY. The product of the two rotations is then the product of reflections in AX, AB, BA, BY. The two middle reflections cancel, and we are left with reflections in AX, BY only. If these lines meet, in C say, the product is accordingly a rotation round C of angle twice $\sphericalangle ACB$. If AX, BY are parallel, the product is a translation.

6. *Groups.* If we have any set of transformations (like the above displacements), which can be combined in pairs, and if the combination of any two of them, say A, B yields a third member of the set, which we may denote by AB, the set is called a *group* of transformations, provided two further conditions are satisfied:

(1) The set must contain the identical transformation I, which makes no change. (Stay put!)

(2) If A is any transformation, the set must contain the inverse of A, that is, a transformation B such that AB and BA are the identical transformation. (If AB = I, B is the transformation: As you were!) Denote the inverse of A by A^{-1}, then AA^{-1} = A^{-1}A = I.

When a group is defined abstractly, we must also assume the associative law: A. BC = AB. C; this is obvious for transformations.

The order in which two transformations are performed may affect the result; AB and BA need not be the same transformation, but if they coincide for all A, B in the group, the group is called *Abelian*.

If A is any displacement, A^{-1} is the displacement which brings all points back to their original position. Displacements in a plane form a group. If R is a reflection, its repetition RR, which we write as R^2, is identity: $R^2 = I$.

If R, S are reflections in lines, RS and SR are not equal, unless the lines are perpendicular.

If T, U be translations then TU = UT.

If X is a displacement, there are pairs of reflections R, S, in lines, such that $X = RS$, $R^2 = S^2 = I$. This is the result in § 4.

7. The product of reflections in two perpendicular lines *OA*, *OB* is particularly simple; if it turns *P* into *R* then *O* is the mid-point of *PR*. The product is a *reflection in a point*.

Some elementary theorems may be restated as follows: The product of reflections in two points *A*, *B* is a translation of amount 2.*AB*; if *ABCD* is a parallelogram, the product of reflections in *A*, *B*, *C*, *D* is identity.

8. A figure is given an *"indirect displacement"* when it is moved in the plane and then turned over; the transformation is the product of a direct displacement and a reflection in a line. Suppose the interval *AB* becomes A_1B_1; complete the parallelogram BAB_1B', then *AB* becomes $B'B_1$ by reflection in the centre *M* of the parallelogram, and we can complete the transformation by reflecting in the bisector of angle $B'B_1A_1$. The reflection in *M* can be resolved into reflections in two lines, one parallel to, and the other perpendicular to that bisector. Thus our indirect displacement is equivalent to a translation followed by a reflection in a line which runs in the direction of the translation.

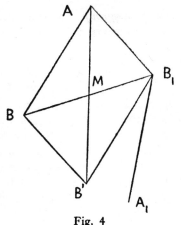

Fig. 4

9. The set of all displacements, direct and indirect, forms a group. The set of direct displacements is a subgroup of this group; its elements are characterized by being products of pairs of reflections in lines.

10. *Homotheties.* We consider another transformation in a plane. Take a fixed point O, and if P be any point, transform it to P_1 on the line OP such that OP_1/OP is constant (independent of the point P chosen). There are two cases, according as P, P_1 are on the same side of O or not. The transformation in both cases is direct; when P describes a circle, P_1 describes another in the same sense. It is clear that this magic-lantern principle enlarges (or contracts) a figure into a similar figure which is similarly placed, that is, if P, R become P_1, R_1, then PR is parallel to P_1R_1.

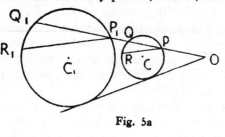

Fig. 5a

We call such figures "*homothetic*", the transformation a "*homothety*"; O is the "*centre*", OP_1/OP the "*ratio*" of the homothety.

If we have two circles and draw their direct common tangents (Fig. 5a), or their transverse common tangents, (Fig. 5b), these meet in points, usually called the "*centres of simili-*

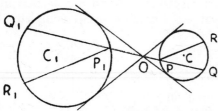

Fig. 5b

tude". These are centres of homotheties that turn one circle into the other. The homothety that turns the circle PQR into the circle $P_1Q_1R_1$, turns the centre C of the first into the centre C_1 of the second, and $OC_1/OC = OP_1/OP$.

11. We give a simple example of a homothety. If through the vertices D, E, F of a triangle DEF, we draw parallels to the opposite sides, these give us a triangle ABC on twice the scale of DEF. The two triangles are homothetic, and A, B, C

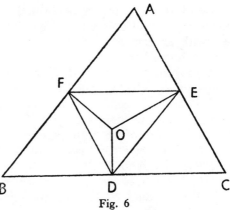
Fig. 6

correspond to D, E, F respectively. The joins AD, BE, CF meet in a point G, say, and the ratios GD/GA, GE/GB, GF/GC are all $\frac{1}{2}$, the constant of the homothety. (The reader may recall that the medians of a triangle meet in a point G such that $GD = \frac{1}{2} GA$, and so on.)

If we draw the "*altitudes*" of DEF, i.e. the lines through the vertices perpendicular to the opposite sides, these lines are also the right bisectors of the sides of triangle ABC, and hence meet in a point O. As DEF was any triangle, it follows that the altitudes of any triangle meet in a point, the "*orthocentre*" of the triangle.

Thus the altitudes of the triangle ABC meet in a point H, its orthocentre, and further $AH = 2OD$, since ABC is on twice the scale of DEF, where O is the circumcentre of ABC. Keep BC fixed and let A describe the circle ABC, then O, D do not move and hence the length of AH, as well as its direction is fixed. Thus the locus of H is the circle obtained from circle ABC by the translation which turns A into H. It can also be regarded as the reflection of circle ABC in BC, or in the mid-point of BC.

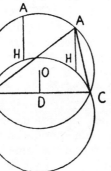
Fig. 7

Returning to triangle ABC, and leaving H fixed, we observe that each of A, B, C, H is the orthocentre of the triangle formed by the other three: we have four "*orthocentric points*"; the circles ABC, BCH, CAH, ABH are congruent.

Now if from any point P we

draw intervals to points on a circle, centre O, radius r, the locus of the mid-points of these intervals is a circle of radius $\frac{1}{2}r$, with its centre at the mid-point of OP. This is a simple case of homothety.

Apply this to the circle ABC, taking H for P, and use the facts given above. The circle ABC is transformed into one of half its radius, with its centre at the mid-point of HO, and it goes through the mid-points of AH, BH, CH, BC, CA, AB and through the feet of the altitudes from A, B, C to the opposite sides.

It is the "*nine point circle*" of ABC, or rather of the four orthocentric points A, B, C, H.

12. It can be shewn (by the theorems of Ceva and Menelaus) that the product of two homotheties is a homothety or a translation. Translations form an abelian group; homotheties and translations together, a non-abelian group.

13. *Similitudes.* If we transform a figure by a homothety, followed by a displacement, or reflection, we get a similar figure. Any transformation which turns figures into similar figures is called a "*similitude*"; "*direct*" if it preserves the sense of rotation, "*indirect*" if it reverses it.

If ABX . . . and $A'B'X'$ . . . be two directly similar polygons, and if by some direct similitude, we change AB into $A'B'$, it is clear that by this transformation ABX . . . will become $A'B'X'$. . . . If AB, $A'B'$ are parallel, the similitude is a homothety. Suppose however they meet in C and that

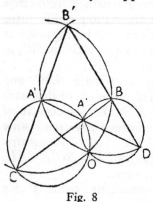

Fig. 8

AA', BB' meet in D. Let the circles $AA'C$, $BB'C$ meet in O. Then from angles in the same segment, we get $\angle AOA' = ACA' = BCB' = BOB'$, and hence $\angle AOB = A'OB'$. Also $\angle OBA = OB'A'$. Thus the triangles OAB, $OA'B'$ are directly similar.

Hence the similitude is the product of a homothety, centre O, and a rotation round the same point.

This might have been expected, but our considerations lead to

a theorem which the reader is asked to retain. If we regard AB, $A'B'$, AA', BB' as any four given lines, they form four triangles of which two, $AA'C$, $BB'C$ have circumcircles which meet in O. The further statement is that the circumcircles of the other two triangles ABD, $A'B'D$ also go through O. *All four meet in that point.*

For since $\not\subset OB'D = OCB = OCA = OA'D$, this is clear for the circle $A'B'D$. Similarly for ABD.

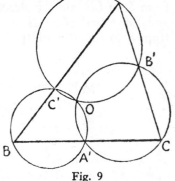

Fig. 9

The theorem can also be shewn from the *Pivot theorem*: if A', B', C' be points on the sides (or sides produced), BC, CA, AB of triangle ABC, then the circles $BC'A'$, $CA'B'$, $AB'C'$ meet in a point.

14. If P be a point on the circumcircle ABC, let X, Z be the feet of the perpendiculars from P to BC, AB. Join XZ and let the line cut AC in Y. Then we know that the circumcircles of ABC, BXZ, AYZ meet in a point, and as the angles BXP, BZP are right angles, the first two circles go through P. Thus P is on the circle AYZ, and since $\not\subset PZA$

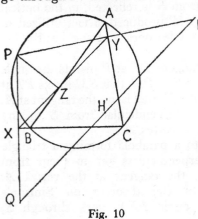

Fig. 10

is a right angle, so is $\not\subset PYA$.

Thus the feet of the perpendiculars from P to the sides of triangle ABC lie on a line, the "*Simson line*" of P for the triangle.

If Q, R be the images of P in BC and CA, it can be shewn that QR goes through H, the orthocentre of ABC.

Thus PH is bisected

by the Simson line of P, as well as by the nine-point circle of ABC.

15. *The parabola*. This is the simplest curve after the circle, and it throws much light on the figures above.

If LR be a fixed line and S a fixed point, let P move so that $SP = PM$, where M is the foot of the perpendicular from P to LR; then P describes a *"parabola"* with *"focus"* S and *"directrix"* LR. If X is the foot of the perpendicular from S to LR, the mid-point A of SX is on the parabola and is its *"vertex"*.

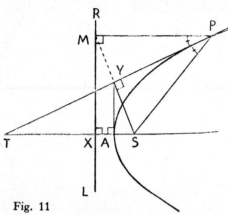

Fig. 11

Now, first, the bisector of the angle SPM is a *"tangent"* to the parabola, that is, it does not meet it except at P; for if Q be any point on it, then $SQ = QM$, whereas if Q were on the parabola, then SQ would equal the perpendicular distance from Q to LM, and this is less than QM.

Hence a ray of light SP from S is reflected, in the optical sense, at P, into a ray along MP produced, a fact utilized in the construction of reflecting telescopes and the head-lights of motor-cars.

Once we know that the tangent PT at P bisects the angle SPM, it follows rapidly, since $SP = PM$, that SM meets PT at right angles at the mid-point of SM, that is, on the tangent at A.

Hence the foot Y of the perpendicular from S to any tangent is on the tangent at the vertex A.

Consider three tangents to a parabola forming a triangle PXY. The feet of the perpendiculars on to them from the focus S lie on a line, the tangent at the vertex A. Hence by the converse of the theorem on Simson's line (which is true), the circle PXY goes through S, and the Simson line of S for triangle PXY is the tangent at A.

We also saw that the join of S to the orthocentre of triangle PXY is bisected by the Simson line of S. Hence that orthocentre is on the directrix of the parabola.

This gives us a construction for the parabola touching four given lines, no three concurrent, no two parallel. If the lines are those in Fig. 8, then O is the focus of the required parabola, and the ortho-centres of the four triangles lie on a line which is its directrix.

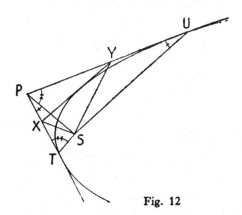

Fig. 12

16. If the tangent XY move round to coincide with TP, the circle $PXYS$ becomes the circle PTS touching PU at P. Hence $\angle STP = SPU$. Similarly $\angle TPS = PUS$.

Hence, if U, T be the points of contact of tangents from P to the parabola, then the triangles STP, SPU are similar, and, in particular $\angle TSP = PSU$.

And since $\angle SXT = SYP$, for S, X, P, Y are concyclic, it follows that $TX/XP = PY/YU$. Thus if X, Y describe similar ranges on TP, PU (as they would if they moved with constant velocities, not necessarily the same), then XY envelops a parabola.

17. *Inversions and antinversions.* The transformations so far considered turn lines into lines, a very important fact which appeared too trivial to mention.

If O is a fixed point, r a fixed number, the transformation which turns P into P' where P, P' are on the same ray from O and $OP. OP' = r^2$, is an "*inversion, centre O, radius r*", or "for the circle, centre O, radius r".

If P, P' be on opposite rays from O and $OP. OP' = r^2$ we have an "antinversion", a product of an inversion and a reflection in O.

If O is the external centre of similitude of two circles, it is the centre of a homothety which relates them, and a line through O which meets one in P, Q will meet the other in corresponding points, say Q', P', where $OP/OQ' = OQ/OP'$ is independent of the line. As OP'. OQ' is also independent of the line, so is OP. OP'. Pursuing this idea, we find that *the inverse of a circle, for a*

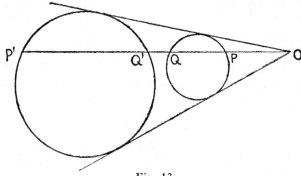

Fig. 13

point, not on it, as centre of inversion, is a circle; and further if the point is on the circle, the inverse is a line. Conversely the inverse of a line for a point not on it, is a circle through the point.

The inverse of a set of parallel lines is a set of circles touching at the centre of inversion.

Both inversion and antinversion are indirect transformations; they reverse the sense of figures.

18. If we invert the figure of the Pivot theorem (Fig. 9), for any centre D, the sides of triangle ABC become circles DBC, DCA, DAB in Fig. 14, and the circles become circles. We get the

Six circles theorem: if A', B, D, C be four points on a circle and circles be drawn through A', B; B, D; D, C; C, A'; and adjacent pairs cut again in C', A, B', D', then these points are concyclic.

The figure is a *"configuration"*, because it is composed of curves, namely circles, and points whereof the same number of curves (three) go through each point, and the same number of points (four) lie on each curve.

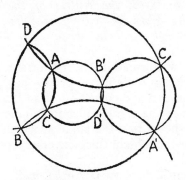

Fig. 14

If we invert Fig. 8 (reproduced here with more convenient letters), for any centre D, we find the figure of the *eight-circles theorem*, like that of the six-circles theorem with the addition of two circles, one through $ABCD'$, one through $A'B'C'D$.

If A, B, C, D' be concyclic, so are A', B', C', D, and conversely.

From Fig. 15, we deduce an unexpected result. If the figure be inverted for centre D', its circles become lines, and its lines become circles through D'. We get a figure which, though not identical with the original, is of the same type. Now when a line is inverted for centre D', the image of D' in the line becomes the centre of the inverse circle. But

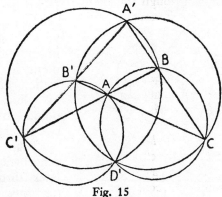

Fig. 15

we know that the images of D' in the four lines lie on a line, that through the orthocentres of the four triangles. This line then inverts into a circle through D' and through the centres of the new circles. The figure being general we have: *the centres of the circumcircles of the four triangles given by four general lines lie on a circle and this goes through the point where these four circumcircles meet.*

19. In any transformation the important thing to notice is, what kinds of figures and properties are unchanged. We have already seen that the collection of all lines and circles in the plane becomes the same collection under inversion; and it can be easily shewn that the angle at which two curves cut equals the angle at which their inverses cut, although the sense is reversed.

Thus, in particular, two *"orthogonal"* circles (circles which cut at right angles), become orthogonal circles or perpendicular lines, or a circle and a line through its centre.

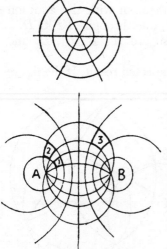

If P, P' be inverse points with respect to a circle, all circles through P, P' cut the circle orthogonally, and this is a characteristic property of such points. It follows that if we invert P, P' and the circle, we get again a circle and two inverse points, or a line and two image points. Inversion of a point in a circle is a generalization of reflection of a point in a line. A line and two image points inverts into a circle and two inverse points.

Take a figure consisting of concentric circles, centre O, and lines through O, and invert it for any point A. The lines

Fig. 16

become circles through A and through B, the inverse of O, except that AO becomes a line. Since the circles in the first figure cut the lines through O at right angles, they become circles which cut all the new circles orthogonally; the exceptional circle through A becomes a line. Thus we get: (1) a set of circles through A, B, (2) a set cutting them orthogonally. Both sets are called *"coaxal"* circles, the lines are the *"radical axes"* of the sets, AB that for the set through A, B. The points A, B are the *"limiting points"* of the second system.

The figure is of great importance in elementary physics.

20. As we can invert the second figure back to the first, we can clearly build it up from any two of its circles, and further, two circles which cut can be inverted into lines (as is obvious); two which do not cut can be inverted into concentric circles.

We make an interesting application. If we have two (non-concentric) circles, one inside the other, and circles are drawn touching them and each other, as in the figure, it may happen that if we continue the ring of touching circles, the last one touches the first; the ring closes. *If this happens once, it will always happen*, whatever be the position of the first circle of the ring. (Steiner.)

To see this we need only invert the main circles into concentric circles, for which the theorem is obvious, and notice that on inverting back, tangent circles become tangent circles.

21. Consider again Fig. 16. The product of reflections in two lines through O is a rotation round O. The product of inversions in two circles, centre O, is a homothety, centre O. Now a line and two image points invert into a circle and two

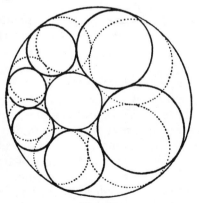

Fig. 17

inverse points. Hence in Fig. 16, the product of inversions in two circles through A, B is analogous to a rotation; for example it could shift area 1 to area 2. The product of inversions in two circles orthogonal to these, is analogous to a homothety; for example it could shift area 2 to area 3.

The second product leaves all circles through A, B invariant; the first, all those orthogonal to these circles. Both leave A, B invariant.

22. *Displacements in three dimensions*. A solid body is moved from one position to another; the points of the body are to be considered as representative points, and its motion is to represent the motion of the whole of space over a stationary space. At present we consider only the initial and the final positions. We then have a transformation of space such that if P, Q become P', Q', then the lengths of PQ and of $P'Q'$ are equal.

First suppose the displacement leaves a point O fixed. Then if A, B be on a sphere, centre O, they become A', B' on the same sphere. Now refer to Fig. 2, and think of it as drawn on the sphere, the lines AB, $A'B'$, AA', BB' being now replaced by great circles, and XP, YP by great circles perpendicular to AA', BB'. The theorems on congruence used in § 4 are valid on the sphere, if lines be replaced by great circles, and we have the result that the displacement leaves P fixed on the sphere.

Hence if a displacement leaves a point O fixed, it leaves some line OP fixed; it is a rotation round a line.

As in the plane, it is easily seen that a translation in space is the product of reflections in two parallel planes, π, π' perpendicular to the direction of translation, and that a rotation is the product of reflections in two planes π, π' through the axis of rotation; in both cases, any plane in the set named may be chosen to play the part either of π or of π'.

The product of reflections in two perpendicular planes is a reflection in the line in which they meet.

Now both the translation and the rotation above are products of reflections in two lines; for interpose a plane π, which for the case of translation is perpendicular to π, π', and, for the rotation, is perpendicular to the axis. The transformation is the product of reflections in π, π_1, then in π_1, π', and each of these pairs gives a reflection in a line. For the translation, these two lines are perpendicular to the direction of translation, and in a plane parallel thereto; for the rotation, they meet the axis at right angles. In both cases either the first line, or the second, can be chosen arbitrarily in the set named.

Consider any displacement in space. If it carries A into A' we split it up into a translation which carries A into A' and a displacement which leaves A' fixed and hence is a rotation. Through A' draw a line l perpendicular both to AA' and to the axis of that rotation. The translation is the product of reflections in two lines of which l may be taken as the *second*; the rotation is the product of reflections in two lines of which l may be taken as the *first*. As the two reflections in l cancel, the whole displacement is the product of reflections in two lines.

Any displacement in space is the product of reflections in two lines.

23. Let these lines be l_1, l_2; if they are parallel, we have a translation. If they are skew, let XY be their common perpendicular, with X on l_1, Y on l_2. Draw l' through Y parallel to l_1. The displacement is the product of reflections in l_1, l', and then in l', l_2, that is of a translation along XY of twice the distance XY, and then a rotation round XY.

The product of a translation along a line and a rotation round that line is called a "*screw*".

Any displacement in space is a screw. Translations and rotations are special cases.

24. *Inversion in space.* If we revolve Fig. 13 round the join of the centres, which goes through O, we get two spheres. We easily prove the following:

The inverse of a sphere, for a point not on it, is a sphere; for a point on it, a plane. The inverse of a plane for a point not on it, is a sphere through the point. The inverse of a set of parallel planes, is a set of spheres touching at the centre of inversion.

As the cut of two spheres is a circle, and it inverts into a cut of two spheres, the inverse of a circle is a circle even when the centre of inversion is not in its plane.

Inversion in space does not change the size of angles.

We can use inversion to deduce a theorem noted by Soddy. Take six equal spheres on a table touching another equal sphere, and draw a plane parallel to the table touching them all. Inverting, we get a ring of six spheres each touching its neighbours, and all touching three other spheres which touch each other; namely the inverse of the middle sphere, of the plane of the table, and of the parallel plane. The theorem is that the

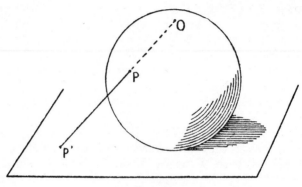

Fig. 18

ring of six spheres in the inverse figure can be started with any sphere touching the other three.

25. Stereographic projection. Project any point P of the sphere from its north pole O on to a point P' on the tangent plane at the south pole. We can choose the radius of inversion so that the inverse of the sphere, for centre O, is that tangent plane, and hence P, P' are inverse points; circles on the sphere project into circles on the plane.

If AB is any line not meeting the sphere, we can draw through it two tangent planes to the sphere, touching it in C, D, say. The lines AB, CD are "*polar lines*" for the sphere. They are obviously at right angles, but there is a further fact, not so obvious. The planes through CD, of course, cut the sphere in circles through C, D; now those planes through AB which cut the sphere cut it in circles orthogonal to (at right angles to), all the circles through C, D. We call both sets of circles, "*coaxal*" circles.

A simple instance is furnished by parallels of latitude and meridian circles; in this case CD goes through the centre, AB is "at infinity".

Now stereographic projection, being an inversion, does not change the size of angles; orthogonal circles become orthogonal circles, or perpendicular lines. Hence if we project our two sets of circles on to the tangent plane, as above, we get a set of circles through the projections of C, D and another set cutting them orthogonally; we get two orthogonal systems of coaxal circles in a plane.

If we make the projection from the North pole on to the equatorial plane, great circles project into circles which cut the equator diametrically, i.e. at opposite ends of a diameter. They are invariant for the antinversion which leaves the equator invariant.

26. If we take any plane, and invert it into a sphere, the lines and circles on the plane become circles on the sphere. But as, on the sphere, a circle is cut out by a plane, we can enter three-dimensional geometry.

Take Fig. 15 and invert it to a figure on a *sphere*. We get eight points A, A', B, B', C, C', D, D', where D is the centre of inversion. The tetrahedron $ABCD$ is such that A', B', C', D' are on its faces BCD, CAD, ABD, ABC respectively, while the tetrahedron A', B', C', D' is such that A, B, C, D are on the faces $B'C'D'$, $C'A'D'$, $A'B'D'$, $A'B'C'$ respectively.

Tetrahedra so related are called "*Möbius pairs*".

27. *The Argand diagram.* We assume the reader has met the method which represents the complex number $x + iy$ by the point in the plane whose co-ordinates are (x, y).

The operation of adding a number $a + ib$ corresponds to the translation which moves the origin to the point (a, b), since (x, y) becomes $(x + a, y + b)$.

Multiplication by $r(\cos \theta + i \sin \theta)$ corresponds to the homothety, centre the origin, ratio r, and a rotation round the origin of angle θ; for this multiplication turns $k (\cos \alpha + i \sin \alpha)$ into $kr [\cos (\alpha + \theta) + i \sin (\alpha + \theta)]$, and so the point

$$(k \cos \alpha, k \sin \alpha) \text{ becomes the point}$$
$$(kr \cos (\alpha + \theta), kr \sin (\alpha + \theta)).$$

The homothety, centre a, ratio r, changes z into z' where $z' - a = r (z - a)$. We can deduce (§ 12) that the product of two homotheties is a homothety or a translation.

The transformation of z into $z' = 1/z$ is the product of an inversion in a circle, centre O, of unit radius, and a reflection in the x-axis.

For if $z = r (\cos \theta + i \sin \theta)$ then $1/z = \dfrac{1}{r}(\cos \theta - i \sin \theta)$

Transformations of the form $z' = az + b$, (a, b constants) are similitudes; the centre of similitude is $b/(1 - a)$.

Any transformation of the form $z' = (az + b) / (cz + d)$, where a, b, c, d, are any constants, real or complex, with $ad - bc \neq 0$, can be broken up into transformations thus:

$$z_1 = cz, \quad z_2 = z_1 + d, \quad z_3 = 1/z_2,$$
$$z_4 = \frac{1}{c}(bc - ad) z_3, \quad z' = z_4 + a/c.$$

Each of those is the product of an even number of reflections in lines and inversions in circles; hence so is the "*linear fractional*" transformation above—which is their product.

There are, in general, just two points which the transformation does not change.

If $z = x + iy$ we denote its "*conjugate*" $x - iy$ by $\bar{z}$. Then $z' = 1/\bar{z}$ is an inversion.

It can be shewn that any *circular transformation* in the plane, that is, any transformation which turns points into points, and the set of all lines and circles into the same set, is represented by a linear fractional transformation, if it is direct, and by z' equal to a linear fractional transformation of $\bar{z}$ if it is indirect, and that it can be expressed as a product of at most four, or at most three, inversions in circles and reflections in lines, in these two cases respectively.

Things go more smoothly in the theory of inversion if we regard a straight line as a special kind of circle, and invent an extra "point of infinity" through which all lines are supposed to pass. This point corresponds to the point O on the sphere in the stereographic projection (Fig. 18), and when it is added to the plane, we speak of an "inversion plane", and of "inversion geometry".

27a. We saw in § 18 that if four lines be given in general position (i.e. no three concurrent, no two parallel) then

> (i) The circum-circles of the four triangles meet in a *point*, which call P_4 and
>
> (ii) The circum-centres lie on a circle, which call C_4. The fact that P_4 lies on C_4 we now ignore.

Suppose five lines be given in general position. If we leave out each in turn we get five sets of four lines and these give five *points* like P_4 in (i). These five points lie on a *circle*; call it K_5. If six lines be given and we omit each in turn, we get six sets of five lines and each set gives a circle like K_5. These six circles go through a point P_6, and so on for seven lines and indefinitely: *point* and *circle* occur alternately. This generalizes (1).

The generalization of (ii) proceeds more smoothly. If five lines be given we get five circles like C_4. They go through one point and their centres lie on a circle, C_5 say. If six lines be given we get six circles like C_5. They go through a point and their centres lie on a circle C_6. And so on.

In special cases we may have lines instead of some of the circles.

CHAPTER II

AN INTRODUCTION TO PLANE CURVES

28. THE reader will be familiar with the elements of graph work where perpendicular axes are used. A point in the plane is then represented by two co-ordinates x, y, the distances, with appropriate signs, of the point from the axes.

If the point (x, y) moves so that it satisfies an equation of the first degree, $lx + my + n = 0$, where l, m, n are constants, it describes a straight line. The ratios $l : m : n$ determine the line.

The simplest equations of the second degree have the forms:
$$y^2 = 4ax,$$
$$x^2/a^2 + y^2/b^2 = 1,$$
$$x^2/a^2 - y^2/b^2 = 1,$$
where a, b, are constants.

An equation of the second degree, $f(x, y) = 0$, will represent a pair of straight lines, when $f(x, y)$ factorizes into two linear factors; if this is not the case, then by appropriate choice of axes, the equation can be reduced to one of the forms above. These represent respectively a parabola, an ellipse with semi-axes a, b, and a hyperbola with semi-axes a, b. These can be obtained as plane sections of a cone on a circular base, and hence are called "*conics*".

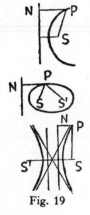

First investigated by the Greeks, they found an application two thousand years later, when Newton proved that a particle attracted to a central body by gravitation describes a conic.

A conic can be defined as the locus of a point P which moves so that its distance from a given point S, the "*focus*", has a fixed ratio to its distance from a fixed line, the corresponding "*directrix*". The ratio is the "*eccentricity*" e; if $e = 1$, we have the parabola discussed in Chap. I. If $e < 1$, we have an

Fig. 19

ellipse, and if $e > 1$, a hyperbola. These curves have two foci S, S' and as P moves on the ellipse, SP, $S'P$ have a constant sum; as P moves on the hyperbola, they have a constant difference. The hyperbola has two *"asymptotes"*, lines which it approaches at great distances.

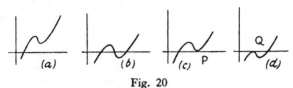

Fig. 20

29. A curve with an equation
$$y = ax^3 + bx^2 + cx + d \qquad (1)$$
may have two points at which the tangent is parallel to the x-axis; their x-co-ordinates are the roots of the quadratic obtained from (1) by differentiation:
$$3ax^2 + 2bx + c = 0, \qquad (2)$$
If this quadratic has real roots, we get Figs. 20 a,b,c,d according to whether the curve cuts the x-axis in one or three points (of which two may coincide). We take $a > 0$.

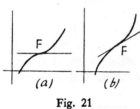

Fig. 21

If the quadratic (2) has two coincident roots, the curve has a *"point of inflexion"* or a *"flex"* F (Fig. 21a); if it has no real roots, the curve continually rises (since $a > 0$) and has a flex F with the tangent there inclined to the x-axis (Fig. 21b.)

30. The equation
$$y^2 = ax^3 + bx^2 + cx + d$$
also represents a *"cubic"* curve, since like the last it is given by

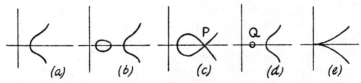

Fig. 22

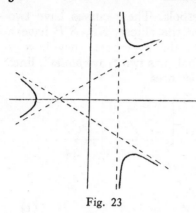

Fig. 23

an equation of the third degree. Corresponding to Figs. 20, *a,b,c,d* we get the shapes in Figs. 22, *a,b,c,d*.

The curves in Figs. (*a*), (*b*), have two visible flexes; in Fig. (*c*) we have a "*double-point*" or "*node*". In Fig. (*d*), the curve has an "*isolated point*" Q. (These points correspond to *P*, *Q*, in Fig. 20 (*c*), (*d*).

The curve $y^2 = x^3$ (Fig. 22 (*e*) presents another peculiarity: there is a sharp point or "*cusp*" at the origin.

Nodes, cusps, and isolated points are the simplest types of "*singular points*", or "*singularities*".

No line can cut a conic in more than two points, or a cubic in more than three. A conic can have only two asymptotes, if any, but a cubic may have three, for example (Fig. 23).

$$x (3y^2 - x^2) + a(x^2 + y^2) = 0$$

or in polars $r \cos 3\theta = a.$

The curve $(x^2 + y^2) (x + 3) - 4 = 0$

has an "*inflexional asymptote*" (Fig. 24); the curve approaches it on the same side from both ends, whereas for the usual type of asymptote, it approaches it from opposite sides (Fig. 19).

31. Another way in which the shapes of curves can be investigated is by the variation of coefficients of an equation. Consider two ellipses $F_1 = 0$, $F_2 = 0$, which cut in four points. Together they constitute a "*quartic*" curve $F_1F_2 = 0$, or one whose equation is of the fourth degree. If we multiply F_1F_2 out, and slightly vary the coefficients, we get a quartic which hugs the ellipses. There are two possible forms, one consisting

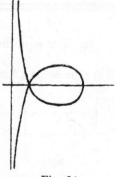

Fig. 24

of four beans, the other (dotted) of two circuits, one inside the other. A line which touches a curve in two points is a *"bitangent"*. Inspection of the figure reveals that each bean of the first quartic has a bitangent, and that two beans have four common tangents which must be counted as bitangents of

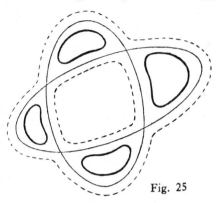

Fig. 25

the quartic. In all we have $4 + 4.6 = 28$ bitangents, which, as we shall see later, is the greatest number that a quartic can have.

In the same way, from an ellipse and a line cutting it, we can get cubics with the forms above; but the variety of shapes which quartics and even cubics can assume is quite bewildering and more powerful methods, discussed later, are necessary.

32. Other curves arise when we consider moving bodies. If a circle rolls on the outside of another, a point on it describes an *"epicycloid"*. Such curves were used by the Greeks to describe planetary motions, and later were used in designing the shape of toothed wheels.

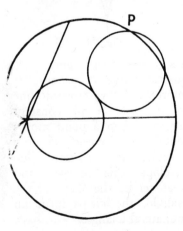

P

If the circles have equal radii, we get a *"cardioid"* (Fig. 26), a quartic curve with a cusp. Any line through the cusp is cut by the curve in an interval of fixed length.

Again if the rolling circle has radius half that of the fixed circle we get a curve with two cusps, a portion of which is seen as a bright curve when the sun shines on a cup of tea. A cardioid would be seen if the source of light were on the rim

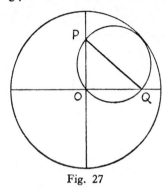

Fig. 27

of the cup for then the rays after reflection at the cup, would touch a cardioid.

If we roll a circle *inside* a fixed circle, and the moving circle has half the radius of the fixed circle, each of its points describes a diameter; opposite points P, Q describe perpendicular diameters; any point on PQ describes an ellipse (the mid-point, a circle).

The envelope of PQ is an "*astroid*" (Fig. 28), a curve of degree six with four visible cusps. (The "*envelope*" of a moving curve is a curve touching all positions of the moving curve.) The astroid is also obtained as the locus of a point on a circle rolling inside a fixed circle of four times its radius. Its equation is $x^{2/3} + y^{2/3} = a^{2/3}$, $(a = OA)$.

If the rolling circle has radius one-third of that of the fixed circle, the locus

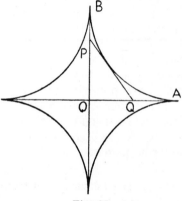

Fig. 28

has three cusps and is a quartic curve (Fig. 29). It intercepts any tangent line in an interval of constant length. When a point moves round the circumcircle of a triangle, its Simson line envelops this curve, and whatever be the shape of the triangle, the cusps form an equilateral triangle.

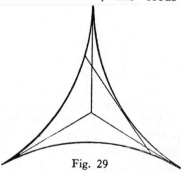

Fig. 29

33. Sooner or later, a little differential calculus is needed in the study of curves. Let s be the length of the arc of a curve to a point P measured from a fixed point on the curve, and ψ be the angle between the tangent at P and a fixed direction (Fig. 30) then $\rho = ds/d\psi$ is the *"radius of curvature"* at P and $1/\rho$ is the *"curvature"*. If Q, R be points on the curve, one on each side of P, the circle QPR will, at usual points on our curves, tend to a certain circle as Q, R tend to P, and this circle has radius ρ. Its centre is the *"centre of curvature"* of

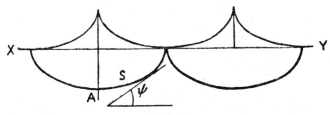

Fig. 30

the curve at P. It lies on the *"normal"* at P, i.e. on the perpendicular to the tangent at P.

When a wheel rolls on a straight line, a point on the rim describes a *"cycloid"*, a curve made up of arches (Fig. 30), the curve below the line XY; the figure has been turned upside down). If s be measured from the bottom point A of an arch, and ψ from a horizontal line, then on the same arch, $s = 4a \sin \psi$, where a is the radius of the rolling circle.

If a piece of string be wrapped round a curve and then unwound, its end point describes an *"involute"* of the curve. For example, if we unwind cotton from a cotton-reel, keeping the cotton tight, the end point of the cotton describes an involute of a circle, a curve which is now used for the design of toothed wheels.

It is easy to see that the locus of the centres of curvature of an involute of a curve is the original curve; the locus of the centres of curvature of any curve is called its *"evolute"*.

The evolute of the cycloid (Fig. 30) is an equal cycloid,

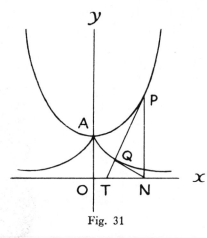

Fig. 31

the curve above the line *XY*. This fact was used by Huygens (1656) in the construction of pendulum clocks. If the bob of a pendulum is made to describe a cycloid, the time of oscillation is independent of the amplitude, which is not the case if the bob describes a circle, and we can make the bob describe a cycloid by using cycloidal checks for the supporting string.

34. A uniform chain hung up under gravity takes the form of a *"catenary"*, a curve with equation $y = c$ ch x/c, where* the *x*-axis is at a distance $c = OA$ below the curve; the *x*-axis is called the *"directrix"* of the catenary. Let $\angle PTN = \psi$.

If *s* be measured from its lowest point *A*, then

$$s = c \text{ sh } x/c = c \tan \psi, \quad y = c \sec \psi, \quad \rho = c \sec^2 \psi.$$

If *PT* is the tangent, *PR* the normal, *PN* the perpendicular to the *x*-axis, where *T*, *R*, *N* are on the *x*-axis, and *Q* the foot of the perpendicular from *N* to *PT*, it can be shewn that, as *P* varies, *NQ* has the constant length *c*, and that $PQ = s$, $PR = \rho$.

The locus of *Q*, as *P* varies, is an involute of the catenary, called the *"tractrix"*, a curve with a cusp at *A*, and with the *x*-axis as asymptote. The tangential interval *QN* has constant length *c*.

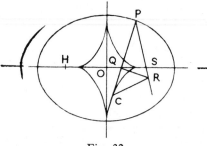

Fig. 32

* ch *x* and sh *x* are defined as follows:
  ch $x = 1 + x^2/2! + x^4/4! + \ldots = \frac{1}{2}(e^x + e^{-x})$
  sh $x = x + x^3/3! + x^5/5! + \ldots = \frac{1}{2}(e^x - e^{-x})$

35. We give two interesting constructions for the centre of curvature of an ellipse, foci S, H, centre O, at a point P.

(1) Let the normal at P cut SH in Q, and the perpendicular at Q to PQ cut SP in R. Then the perpendicular to SP at R cuts PQ in the centre of curvature C for the point P.

(2) If the perpendicular to PQ at Q cuts OP in T, then TC is perpendicular to SH.

As P moves round the ellipse, the locus of the centres of curvature, the evolute of the ellipse, is a curve like an astroid with unequal axes (Fig. 28). It is shewn in Fig. 32, inside the ellipse. The evolute of a parabola is like Fig. 22 (*e*).

35*a*. We can of course invert a conic, given a fixed centre of inversion O and fixed radius r as on p. 19. Then if P describes a conic, P' describes the inverse figure. We give some special cases.

(i) The inverse of a parabola when the centre of inversion is at its focus, is a cardioid.

(ii) The inverse of a rectangular hyperbola (p. 49) when the centre of inversion is at its centre is a curve like a figure of eight, the "*lemniscate* of Bernoulli", an arc of which is now used by designers of roads for fast traffic.

A very interesting connection between the catenary and parabola is used later (p. 145). If we roll a parabola on a straight line its focus describes a catenary. If we roll an ellipse along a line its focus describes a curve with loops, but a hyperbola gives a wavy curve.

CHAPTER III

CO-ORDINATE GEOMETRY

36. In the method of co-ordinate geometry, we reduce a question in geometry to one in algebra, but if this is done in a straightforward and obvious way, we often encounter involved algebra even if the geometrical question is simple. We must devise economical methods.

The kind of problem which gave rise to co-ordinate Geometry (Descartes, 1637) was of this nature: what is the locus of a point which moves so that the product of its distances from two given lines is in a constant ratio to the product of its distances from two others?

Now the distance of a point (x', y') from the line

$$ax + by + c = 0 \qquad (1)$$

is known to be

$$(ax' + by' + c)/(a^2 + b^2)^{\frac{1}{2}}$$

and hence, if the lines have form (1), with coefficients (a_1, b_1, c_1), (a_2, b_2, c_2), (a_3, b_3, c_3) and (a_4, b_4, c_4) respectively, the equation of the locus will be, with C constant,

$$\frac{a_1x + b_1y + c_1}{\sqrt{(a_1^2 + b_1^2)}} \cdot \frac{a_2x + b_2y + c_2}{\sqrt{(a_2^2 + b_2^2)}} = C \cdot \frac{a_3x + b_3y + c_3}{\sqrt{(a_3^2 + b_3^2)}} \cdot \frac{a_4x + b_4y + c_4}{\sqrt{(a_4^2 + b_4^2)}}$$

If we simplify this, we get an equation of the second degree, and hence the locus is a conic.

37. But if we only wish to know that the locus has an equation of the second degree, it is obvious that we have done much unnecessary work, and as a first step in economy we will represent long expressions by single letters. Write then L_j for $a_jx + b_jy + c_j$ $(j = 1, 2, 3, 4)$. The resulting equation is then

$$L_1L_2 = k\, L_3L_4,$$

where k is some constant, and this is clearly of the second degree unless accidentally the second degree terms cancel.

One instance of this economy is of fundamental importance.

In many problems it is convenient to take as base lines to which everything is referred, not the Cartesian axes x, y, but *three* lines which form a triangle.

If the equation of these lines referred to Cartesian axes as above, be $L_1 = 0$, $L_2 = 0$, $L_3 = 0$, then if (x', y') be substituted for x, y in the expression L_j, we get, say, L'_j, which is a certain definite multiple of the distance of (x', y') from the line $L_j = 0$. *We can treat these multiples of the distances from the lines as co-ordinates*, and write again x, y, z for them. *Which* multiples of the distances are thereby involved will not usually matter in applications of these co-ordinates.

38. *Homogeneous Co-ordinates*. Further economy is achieved by two extensions of the elementary geometry, of which the first is very simple. It is useful in many questions to introduce *points at infinity* and to speak of parallel lines as lines meeting at such a point. We may look on this merely as an extension of the algebra, leaving logical questions till later. If we replace the Cartesian co-ordinates x, y of a point by x'/z, y'/z where z is any number, we call x', y', z the "*homogeneous*" Cartesian co-ordinates; the point is fixed uniquely by their *ratios*. Dropping the dash, we shall say (x, y, z) are the homogeneous Cartesian co-ordinates of a point, when $(x/z, y/z)$ are the usual co-ordinates.

The equation of a line is now of the form $ax + by + cz = 0$; the point (x', y', z') is on it, if $ax' + by' + cz' = 0$.

Now in ordinary Cartesians, the lines $a_1 x + b_1 y + c_1 = 0$ and $a_2 x + b_2 y + c_2 = 0$ are parallel if $a_1/a_2 = b_1/b_2$ holds. But here the corresponding equations, $a_1 x + b_1 y + c_1 z = 0$ and $a_2 x + b_2 y + c_2 z = 0$, are both satisfied by $z = 0$, $x/y = -b_1/a_1$, if $a_1/a_2 = b_1/b_2$. Hence we may say that parallel lines meet on $z = 0$; or that $z = 0$ is the equation of the "*line at infinity*".

As only the ratios of co-ordinates matter, we can always put $z = 1$, if we wish, for points not on the line at infinity, but not for points that do lie on that line. "Infinity," said the boy, "is where things happen which don't."

Homogeneous Cartesians may now be regarded as a special case of the co-ordinates of § 37, the lines L_1, L_2, L_3 being replaced by the x, y axes and the line at infinity. The distance interpretation in that section does not now apply; it is a ladder which must often be discarded.

39. Reconsider our reference triangle: the equations of its sides in homogeneous Cartesian co-ordinates (x, y, z) are, say

$$a_i x + b_i y + c_i z = 0, \quad (i = 1, 2, 3).$$

If (x, y, z) be the homogeneous Cartesian co-ordinates of a point, then its co-ordinates with respect to the triangle are (x', y', z'), where

$$\begin{aligned} x' &= a_1 x + b_1 y + c_1 z, \\ y' &= a_2 x + b_2 y + c_2 z, \\ z' &= a_3 x + b_3 y + c_3 z. \end{aligned} \quad (1)$$

In particular, as only ratios are relevant, the co-ordinates of the vertices of the reference triangle can be taken as $(1, 0, 0)$, $(0, 1, 0)$, $(0, 0, 1)$.

The condition that the sides of the triangle do not meet in a point is that the determinant* of the coefficients on the right-hand side of (1) does not vanish. The equations can then be solved, and x, y, z expressed as linear functions of x', y', z'.

If we take three linear functions of x', y', z' with non-zero determinant, these are also linear functions of x, y, z with non-zero determinant, and hence are a possible set of co-ordinates. We can now forget, if we wish, that (x, y, z) in (1) were homogeneous Cartesians, and suppose them to be any set of homogeneous co-ordinates. The lack of rigidity in the homogeneous co-ordinates must be noticed: if (x, y, z) is one set, so is (x', y', z') where $x' = h_1 x$, $y' = h_2 y$, $z' = h_3 z$, the h_i being any constants.

40. There is then another way of regarding equations (1). Keep the triangle of reference for x, y, z *fixed*. Then these equations connect the co-ordinates of the point (x, y, z) with those of another point, (x', y', z'). We may say they *"transform"* the point (x, y, z) into the point (x', y', z'). In Morley's suggestive phrase we have an *alibi*; before we had an *alias*. We mentioned that, if (1) holds, then also x, y, z are linear functions of x', y', z'; hence if the point (x, y, z) describes a line, so that the co-ordinates (x, y, z) satisfy a linear equation, then the point (x', y', z') describes a line.

---

* The determinant is $a_1 (b_2 c_3 - b_3 c_2) + b_1 (c_2 a_3 - c_3 a_2) + c_1 (a_2 b_3 - a_3 b_2)$.

Thus the transformation turns lines into lines, and we call it a *"collineation"*. We must remember that, in view of its origin, we assumed the determinant of the coefficients of the set of equations (1) was not zero; if it were zero, *all* lines could be transformed into lines through some fixed point, the collineation is then *"degenerate"*.

It is clear from the algebra that all non-degenerate collineations form a group, the *"collineation-group"*. Degenerate collineations do not have an inverse. (Cf. § 6). In Chapter I displacement, homotheties, similitudes, reflections in lines were collineations.

41. Suppose in any co-ordinates, homogeneous or not, that $U = o$, $V = o$ are the equations of any curves, then $U + kV = o$ (k constant) represents a curve going through all points common to $U = o$ and $V = o$; for if the co-ordinates of a point satisfy $U = o$ and $V = o$, they satisfy $U + kV = o$. There are few remarks so trivial that are so important. When we vary k, the curves $U + kV = o$ form a *"pencil"*.

If U, V be lines (we mean by that, if $U = o$, $V = o$ be the equations of lines, and so of the first degree), then $U + kV$ is a line through their cut, or a line parallel to them, if they are parallel.

If U, V, W be lines, and $k_1U + k_2V + k_3W = o$ identically, where k_1, k_2, k_3 do not all vanish, then U, V, W concur; for if $k_3 \neq o$, then $W = -(k_1/k_3)U - (k_2/k_3)V$.

In ordinary Cartesians, an equation $U = o$ of the *second* degree, in which the coefficients of x^2 and y^2 are both unity, and which contains no xy term, represents a circle, and if (x', y') be substituted in U, we get the "power" of (x', y') for the circle, that is, the square of the distance of (x', y') from the centre minus the square of the radius.

If U, V be circles, then $U - V$ is a straight line through their cuts, if they cut, and in any case it is the locus of points whose powers for U, V are equal, the *"radical axis"* of U, V; while $U + kV$ ($k \neq -1$) is another circle through their cuts, if they cut, and in any case is the locus of points whose powers for U, V are in a constant ratio, a circle *"coaxal"* with U, V. (These notions agree with those introduced in § 19.)

If W is another circle,* then
$$(U - V) + (V - W) + (W - U) = 0,$$
and hence the radical axes of pairs of U, V, W concur, in the "*radical centre*" of U, V, W.

42. *Imaginary points.* The second of the extensions mentioned in § 38 will now be considered. At first sight it looks like wanton mystification, but it leads to a miraculous economy. The logical justification is postponed. "Mathematics has nothing to do with mysteries, except to remove them."

If two circles cut in two points, we can solve for the co-ordinates of the points and find the equation of the line joining them; if, however, we take the circles
$$x^2 + y^2 - 4 = 0, \; x^2 + y^2 - 2x - 2y = 10$$
we find for the co-ordinates of the cuts $(-\tfrac{3}{2} \pm \tfrac{1}{2} \sqrt{-1},$ $-\tfrac{3}{2} \mp \tfrac{1}{2} \sqrt{-1})$ to which, at present, no points correspond. Notwithstanding this, if we now use the algebraical method for finding the equation of the line joining these "points", we get $x + y + 3 = 0$, the equation of the radical axis of the circles, just as we should if the circles actually cut.

Let us restore the parallelism between the languages of geometry and of algebra by saying that the circles cut in "imaginary points", whose co-ordinates involve $\sqrt{-1}$, and that the join of these points is a "real" line, the radical axis.

We shall work with imaginary points when we wish, regarding the ordinary plane of points with real co-ordinates as immersed in a plane of points whose co-ordinates may be complex numbers. Then if we reach a statement which involves only real figures, this will be true, even though in deducing it, we have used imaginary points.

43. *Cross-ratio.* If $L = 0$, $M = 0$ be equations of lines in any system of co-ordinates then $L + kM = 0$ is a line through their common point; let us call k the "parameter" of the line, we see that it fixes the line in terms of L, M. If instead of L, M we take another pair of lines for base-lines, say $aL + bM = 0$, and $a'L + b'M = 0$, through the common point, then $L + kM = 0$ will be represented by
$$(aL + bM) + k'(a'L + b'M) = 0, \text{ also,}$$

* The coefficients of x^2 and y^2 in U, V, W, are supposed to be unity.

provided $k = \dfrac{b + k'b'}{a + k'a'}$, or $k' = -\dfrac{b - ka}{b' - ka'}$

But although k depends on the "base-lines", yet if we have four lines with parameters k_1, k_2, k_3, k_4 their "*cross-ratio*", defined as $(k_1 - k_2)(k_3 - k_4)/(k_2 - k_3)(k_4 - k_1)$, is independent of the base-lines; this will be plain if it is shewn that the cross-ratio is not changed when the k are subject to the transformation $k' = \dfrac{ak + b}{ck + d}$, $(ad - bc \neq 0)$.

The notation has been changed so that comparison may be made with § 27, where this transformation was broken up into simpler ones. It is very easy to verify that these simple transformations do not change the cross-ratio.

Again if, by a collineation, the lines L, M, $L + kM$ are transformed to L', M', $L' + k'M'$, then the cross-ratio of four values of k equals that of the corresponding four values of k'. This is a very important fact.

44. It is convenient when we use homogeneous co-ordinates to denote the points with co-ordinates (x, y, z), (x_1, y_1, z_1), (x', y', z'), by P, P_1, P', and so on Any point on the line through P_1, P_2 has co-ordinates of form $(x_1 + kx_2, y_1 + ky_2, z_1 + kz_2)$ for a suitable k, and may be denoted by $P_1 + kP_2$. We can define the "*cross-ratio*" of the four points $P_1 + k_1P_2$, $P_1 + k_2P_2$, $P_1 + k_3P_2$, $P_1 + k_4P_2$ of the line P_1P_2 by the same function of the k as in § 43, and as there, we can shew that it is independent of the "base-points" P_1, P_2.

We may call (l_1, m_1, n_1) the "co-ordinates" of the line $l_1x + m_1y + n_1z = 0$; only their ratios are relevant. Any line through the point where the lines (l_1, m_1, n_1) and (l_2, m_2, n_2) meet, has co-ordinates $(l_1 + kl_2, m_1 + km_2, n_1 + kn_2)$ for suitable k.

It is now easy to shew that the cross-ratio of any four concurrent lines equals that of the four points in which they cut any line, and that these cross-ratios are not changed by collineations.

When the cross-ratio is -1, the four points, or four lines, form a "*harmonic range*" and "*harmonic pencil*" respectively.

Thus P_1, $P_1 + lP_2$, P_2, $P_1 + mP_2$ form a harmonic range, if $l/m = -1$, and as only the ratios of co-ordinates are relevant, and so (x_2, y_2, z_2) and (lx_2, ly_2, lz_2) represent the same point, we can choose co-ordinates so that the four points of a given harmonic range are represented by P_1, $P_1 + P_2$, P_2, $P_1 - P_2$. Any other point of the line is then represented by $l_1 P_1 + l_2 P_2$ for suitable l_1, l_2, and l_1/l_2 fixes it.

45. *Imaginary lines and conics.* An imaginary line is the set of points (x, y, z), real or not, which satisfy an equation $ax + by + cz = 0$, where a, b, c may be real or complex numbers. This line always contains at least one real point. For if $a = a_1 + ia_2$, and so on, the equation becomes $a_1 x + b_1 y + c_1 z + i(a_2 x + b_2 y + c_2 z) = 0$, and there are real ratios $x : y : z$ such that

$$a_1 x + b_1 y + c_1 z = 0, \quad a_2 x + b_2 y + c_2 z = 0.$$

A quadratic equation with real coefficients, which is satisfied by no real values of $x : y : z$, not all zero, such as $x^2 + y^2 + z^2 = 0$, can be said to represent an imaginary conic; so can a quadratic with imaginary coefficients, though it may perhaps be satisfied by some real values of $x : y : z$.

Even when we are dealing with real geometry, it is often convenient to remember that equations with real coefficients can be satisfied by points with complex co-ordinates, so that these may be regarded as imaginary points on the curve. Thus if x_1, y_1, z_1 and x_2, y_2, z_2 satisfy $ax + by + cz = 0$, so do $x_1 + ix_2, y_1 + iy_2, z_1 + iz_2$.

46. *General Conic.* We now move more rapidly and the reader may prefer to turn to the next Chapter.

Consider the general equation of the second degree:

$$ax^2 + by^2 + cz^2 + 2fyz + 2gzx + 2hxy = 0, \qquad (1)$$

or $S = 0$, where the coefficients may be real or complex.

The line $P_1 P_2$ cuts the conic at the point $P_1 + kP_2$, if k is chosen so that the co-ordinates of this point satisfy (1). Substituting, we get for this condition the equation

$$S_{11} + 2kS_{12} + k^2 S_{22} = 0, \qquad (2)$$

where

$$S_{11} = ax_1^2 + by_1^2 + cz_1^2 + 2fy_1 z_1 + 2gz_1 x_1 + 2hx_1 y_1,$$
$$S_{12} = ax_1 x_2 + by_1 y_2 + cz_1 z_2$$
$$+ f(y_1 z_2 + y_2 z_1) + g(z_1 x_2 + z_2 x_1) + h(x_1 y_2 + x_2 y_1).$$
$$S_{22} = ax_2^2 + by_2^2 + cz_2^2 + 2fy_2 z_2 + 2gz_2 x_2 + 2hx_2 y_2$$

S_{12} is a *bilinear form*; its method of construction from S is clear.

We shall write

$X = ax + hy + gz, Y = hx + by + fz, Z = gx + fy + cz,$
$X_1 = ax_1 + hy_1 + gz_1$ and so on for Y_1, Z_1, X_2, Y_2, Z_2
Then it will be found that

$S_{12} = x_1X_2 + y_1Y_2 + z_1Z_2 = x_2X_1 + y_2Y_1 + z_2Z_1 = S_{21}.$

47. If the roots of the quadratic in k are equal and opposite, then $S_{12} = 0$. But if these roots be $\pm \alpha$, P_1P_2 will cut the conic in $P_1 \pm \alpha P_2$, that is, in points which separate P_1, P_2 harmonically.

P_1, P_2 are then called "*conjugate*" points for the conic. Fixing P_1, let P_2 vary, then the locus of points P such that P, P_1 are harmonically separated by the cuts of PP_1 and the conic, is the line

$x_1X + y_1Y + z_1Z = 0$ or $xX_1 + yY_1 + zZ_1 = 0.$

This is the "*polar*" of P_1 for the conic; P_1 is the "*pole*" of this line.

Since $S_{12} = S_{21}$, the polar of P_1 goes through P_2, if that of P_2 goes through P_1. (The reciprocal property.)

Two points are conjugate for a conic when the polar of each goes through the other; two lines when the pole of each lies on the other.

If tangents can be drawn from point P to the conic, the polar of P is the line through their points of contact. If P is on the conic its polar is the tangent at P.

48. The line P_1P_2 touches the conic if (2) has equal roots in k; the condition is $S_{11}S_{22} = S_{12}^2$.

Keeping P_1 fixed, let P_2 vary, and we find

$(ax_1^2 + by_1^2 + \ldots)(ax^2 + by^2 + \ldots) = (axx_1 + byy_1 + \ldots)^2$

for the locus of all points P such that P_1P touches the conic.

It can be remembered as Conic $\times$ Conic$_1$ = Polar^2, and is the equation of the pair of tangents from P_1 to the conic.

49. Consider four lines L, M, N, R forming a quadrilateral, with equations $L = 0$, and so on. If we take LMN as the reference triangle, $R = 0$ will be an equation

$k_1L + k_2M + k_3N = 0$

for some k_i. Since $k_1L = 0$ and $L = 0$ give the same line, we can "absorb" multipliers and take as the equation of R: $L + M + N = 0$; adjusting the sign of R we have the identity $L + M + N + R = 0$ between the equations of the four lines $L = 0, \ldots, R = 0$.

The line $L + N = 0$ goes through D, the cut of L, N; but its equation can be written $M + R = 0$, hence it goes through B, the cut of M, R, and hence it is the line BD. Similarly $N + M = 0$ is the line AC, and $L + M = 0$ is the line EF.

$(L + N) - (N + M) = 0$, or $L - M = 0$, goes through the cut K of BD and AC, and through E, the cut of L, M.

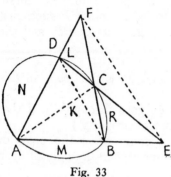

Fig. 33

Hence it is the line EK.

Since EF, EK have equations $L \pm M = 0$, they form with L, M a harmonic pencil; this is the harmonic property of the quadrilateral $LMNR$.

The pair of lines L, M together constitute a degenerate conic with equation $LM = 0$.

Consider a conic with equation $LM = kNR$. It is of the type $U - kV = 0$ where U is the line-pair L, M, and V the line-pair N, R, and hence it goes through the four points A, B, C, D, where the line-pairs cut each other. It is the equation given by our first problem in § 37.

The bilinear form in (x, y, z) and (x_1, y_1, z_1) which corresponds to LM is $LM_1 + L_1 M$, where L_1 is the result of substituting (x_1, y_1, z_1) in the expression L. Hence the polar of (x_1, y_1, z_1) for the conic $LM = kNR$ is

$$LM_1 + L_1 M = k(NR_1 + N_1 R).$$

Take (x_1, y_1, z_1) at the point E, then $L_1 = M_1 = 0$, and the polar is $R_1 N + N_1 R = 0$ and hence goes through F. Similarly, or by the reciprocal property (§ 47), the polar of F goes through E.

If we take (x_1, y_1, z_1) at K, then $L_1 + N_1 = 0$, $N_1 + M_1 = 0$, and hence $L_1 = M_1 = -N_1 = -R_1$. Hence the polar of this point is $L + M = -k(N + R)$, which reduces to $L + M = 0$, the line EF.

Thus the *"diagonal triangle" KEF* of points A, B, C, D is *"self-polar"* for the conic, that is, each vertex is the pole of the opposite side.

50. If two conics meet in four distinct points, real or imaginary, we can take them for the points A, B, C, D above, and get a triangle self-polar for both conics. Take this triangle as the triangle of reference. The polar of the vertex $(1, 0, 0)$ for a conic given by the general equation § 46 (1), is $ax + hy + gz = 0$, and this has to coincide with $x = 0$. Thus $h = g = 0$. Similarly $f = 0$. Hence the conics when referred to a common self-polar triangle, have equations of form

$$ax^2 + by^2 + cz^2 = 0 \text{ and } a'x^2 + b'y^2 + c'z^2 = 0.$$

51. *Tangential equations.* The line (l, m, n) touches the conic given by the general equation, if there is a point P_1 on the conic at which it is a tangent. As the tangent at P_1 is the polar of P_1, it has the equation $X_1 x + Y_1 y + Z_1 z = 0$. If this coincides with the line (l, m, n), there must be a constant k such that, writing X_1, Y_1, Z_1 in full,

$$ax_1 + hy_1 + gz_1 = kl,$$
$$hx_1 + by_1 + fz_1 = km,$$
$$gx_1 + fy_1 + cz_1 = kn, \text{ and also}$$
$$lx_1 + my_1 + nz_1 = 0.$$

We assume that the determinant of the coefficients on the left-hand of the first three equations is not zero. We always denote this determinant by Δ. We can then eliminate x_1, y_1, z_1, k from the equations and obtain the tangential equation $\Sigma = 0$, of the conic, the condition that (l, m, n) should touch it.:—

$$Al^2 + Bm^2 + Cn^2 + 2Fmn + 2Gnl + 2Hlm = 0, \quad (1)$$

where $A, B \ldots$ are the co-factors of $a, b \ldots$ in the determinant, namely,

$$A = bc - f^2, \qquad B = ca - g^2, \qquad C = ab - h^2,$$
$$F = gh - af, \qquad G = hf - bg, \qquad H = fg - ch.$$

52. More important for us than this deduction is the result. We began with an equation $S = 0$ in x, y, z which was satisfied when x, y, z were the co-ordinates of a point on the conic, which was regarded as a *locus of points*. We found an

equation $\Sigma = 0$ in l, m, n which was satisfied when l, m, n were the co-ordinates of a line touching the conic, which is then regarded as an *envelope of lines*.

The resemblance between the equations $S = 0$ and $\Sigma = 0$ is clear; each piece of algebra based on one has its counterpart, or *dual* for the other, and to each theorem corresponds a dual theorem (Cf. Chap. IV) We give some instances:

The join of points P_1, P_2 is the line with co-ordinates
$$(y_1z_2 - y_2z_1,\ z_1x_2 - z_2x_1,\ x_1y_2 - x_2y_1).$$
If p_1, p_2 denote the lines (l_1, m_1, n_1) and (l_2, m_2, n_2), their cut is the point
$$(m_1n_2 - m_2n_1,\ n_1l_2 - n_2l_1,\ l_1m_2 - l_2m_1).$$
The polar of P_1 for $S = 0$ is the line (X_1, Y_1, Z_1).

The pole of p_1 for $\Sigma = 0$ is the point (L_1, M_1, N_1), where
$$L_1 = Al_1 + Hm_1 + Gn_1,\quad M_1 = Hl_1 + Bm_1 + Fn_1,$$
$$N_1 = Gl_1 + Fm_1 + Cn_1,$$
$S_1 + kS_2 = 0$ are the conics through the common points of the conics S_1, S_2, one corresponding to each value of k.

$\Sigma_1 + k\Sigma_2 = 0$ are the conics touching the common tangents of the conics Σ_1, Σ_2, one corresponding to each value of k.

If l, m are the polars of P, Q for $S = 0$, then $l + km$ is the polar of $P + kQ$. Hence the cross-ratio of four collinear points equals that of their four polars.

53. *Homogeneous Cartesians.* By § 52, the pole of the line at infinity $z = 0$, or $(0, 0, 1)$, is the point (G, F, C). This is the *"centre"* of the conic; if $C = 0$, then by § 51 (1), $z = 0$ touches the conic. If $C \neq 0$, we have for the centre, the co-ordinates $(G/C, F/C)$ in ordinary Cartesians.

The polar of a point at infinity $(1, m, 0)$ is a *"diameter"* $X + mY = 0$. By the reciprocal property, it goes through the centre, for all m. Hence $X = 0$, $Y = 0$ are the equations for the centre, a point not on the line at infinity if $C \neq 0$.

The polar, $X + mY = 0$, of $(1, m, 0)$ goes through $(1, m', 0)$, if $a + h(m + m') + bmm' = 0$.
The diameters $X + mY = 0$, $X + m'Y = 0$ are then *"conjugate"*, and (if $C \neq 0$), they form with $z = 0$ a self-polar triangle. Taking this as the triangle of reference, the equation of the conic assumes the form $ax^2 + by^2 + cz^2 = 0$.

In particular, when $C \neq 0$, if we take for the triangle of reference the common self-polar triangle of the conic and a circle with the same centre, the conic is referred to its *"principal axes"* and, with $z = 1$, its equation becomes of form $ax^2 + by^2 = 1$, as on p. 30. From this we could regain the focus-directrix definition for the ellipse and hyperbola.

The equation of a conic can be written $xX + yY + zZ = 0$. Hence if it goes through its own centre, and so is a line-pair (p. 46), we have $Z = 0$ when $X = Y = 0$, that is, when $x : y : z = G : F : C$. This gives $gG + fF + cC = 0$, or $\Delta = 0$, for the condition that a conic be a line-pair. Then $X = 0$, $Y = 0$, $Z = 0$ have a common solution x, y, z, the co-ordinates of the point where the lines of the pair meet.

The dual to a line-pair a degenerate conic locus, is a point-pair, a degenerate conic-envelope.

54. *Asymptotes.* A special case of $LM = kNR$ of § 49 arises when $N = R$. Then $LM = kN^2$ is a conic touching L, M at points where they cut N.

The equation of the parabola $y^2 = 4ax$ is, in homogeneous Cartesians, $y^2 = 4axz$. Thus it touches $x = 0$ and $z = 0$ where these meet $y = 0$. Thus it touches the line at infinity, and hence (§ 53), the condition for a parabola is $C = 0$.

If the conic is not a parabola, its asymptotes L, M are tangents at the points where it cuts $z = 0$; thus its equation $S = 0$ has the form $LM - kz^2 = 0$. Thus we get the asymptotes if we take k so that $S + kz^2 = 0$ is a line-pair. Using the condition for a line-pair, we find $k = -\Delta/C$.

The asymptotes are actually parallel to the pair of lines
$$ax^2 + 2hxy + by^2 = 0 \qquad (1)$$
through the origin. This equation has real roots in x/y if $C < 0$, which is hence the condition for a hyperbola, the only conic with real asymptotes.

A hyperbola is *"rectangular"* if its asymptotes are perpendicular. Suppose them parallel to $y = mx$, $y = m'x$; then must $mm' = -1$. If we compare $(y - mx)(y - m'x)$ with (1), we find $a + b = 0$ as the condition that a conic given by the general equation should be a rectangular hyperbola.

If this condition is satisfied by S and S', it is satisfied by

$S + kS'$ for all k. Hence *the conics through the four cuts of two rectangular hyperbolas are all rectangular hyperbolas.* The four cuts are orthocentric points.

55. *The director circle* of a conic is the locus of points (x, y) from which tangents to the conic are perpendicular. Using the equation of the pair of tangents, Conic $\times$ Conic$_1$ = Polar^2, we easily find for the locus the equation

$$C(x^2 + y^2) - 2Gx - 2Fy + A + B = 0,$$
$$\text{or } X^2 + Y^2 = (a + b)S.$$

Thus it is a circle with centre at the centre $(G/C, F/C)$ of the conic. For a parabola, $C = 0$, the circle becomes a line, the directrix. For a rectangular hyperbola, we have a circle of zero radius.

Since $\Sigma_1 + k\Sigma_2$ is a pencil of conics touching four lines, and the equation of the director circle involves the coefficients $A, B, \ldots$ of Σ linearly, we find (§ 41): *The director circles of conics touching four lines are coaxal, or coincident.*

There is one parabola touching four general lines (§ 15): its directrix must be the radical axis of the system of director circles.

56. *Circular points at infinity.* We take a further step in sophistication by combining the ideas of imaginary points and points at infinity.

Compare the hyperbola

$$x^2 - y^2 = az^2, \quad \text{or} \quad (x + y)(x - y) = az^2,$$

and the circle $x^2 + y^2 = az^2$, or $(x + iy)(x - iy) = az^2$.

The tangents to the first at its cuts with $z = 0$ are the asymptotes $x \pm y = 0$; the tangents to the second at its cuts with $z = 0$ are the imaginary lines $x \pm iy = 0$. These are the *"isotropic"* lines through the origin.

Any circle $x^2 + y^2 + 2gx + 2fy + c = 0$, or in homogeneous co-ordinates, $x^2 + y^2 + (2gx + 2fy)z + cz^2 = 0$, meets $z = 0$ at the points where $x^2 + y^2 = 0$ meets it; these points are given by $x \pm iy = 0$, $z = 0$, and hence have co-ordinates $(1, \pm i, 0)$. They are called the *"circular* points *at infinity"* and were discovered at Saratov by General Poncelet, when he was a prisoner of war there after Napoleon's retreat. We denote them by I, J, throughout this book.

If OA, OB by any perpendicular lines, then OA, OI, OB, OJ form a harmonic pencil.

I, J are conjugate points for any rectangular hyperbola.

57. *Foci of a Conic.* The focus-directrix definition of a conic gives the equation, with the origin at the focus,

$$x^2 + y^2 = kN^2, \text{ or } (x + iy)(x - iy) = kN^2,$$

where $N = 0$ is the directrix. Comparing with $LM = N^2$, we see that the conic touches the isotropic lines through the focus, at the (imaginary) points where the directrix cuts the conic. Thus a focus is a cut of a tangent from I and one from J. The two pairs of tangents from I, J yield four such cuts; but if the equation of the conic has real coefficients, only two cuts are real.

To find the equations of the foci, we note that the pair of tangents from $(1, m, 0)$ are given by $SS_1 = \text{polar}^2$, or by

$$S(a + 2hm + bm^2) = (X + mY)^2$$

Taking $m = \pm i$, and adding and subtracting, we get,

$$\frac{X^2 - Y^2}{a - b} = \frac{XY}{h} = S,$$

as equations giving the foci.

The principal axes are given by $h(X^2 - Y^2) = (a - b)XY$.

"*Confocal*" conics are conics with the same foci. It is plain that they are conics touching the same four (imaginary) lines, viz., two through I, two through J.

A parabola touches the line at infinity, IJ; it has only one focus S, and SI, SJ touch the parabola.

58. *Quadratic Transformations.* Two conics through four points referred to their common self-polar triangle (§ 50), have equations

$$ax^2 + by^2 + cz^2 = 0, \quad a'x^2 + b'y^2 + c'z^2 = 0$$

The polars of P_1 for these conics are (ax_1, by_1, cz_1) and $(a'x_1, b'y_1, c'z_1)$, say p_1 and p'_1. The polar of P_1 for $S + kS'$ is $p_1 + kp'_1$.

Hence the polars of a point, for conics through four points, concur. (In an exceptional case, they coincide.)

The dual work gives: the poles of a line for conics which touch four lines, lie on a line; in particular, their centres lie on a line which must go through the mid-points of the diagonals of the quadrilateral made up by the four lines.

Resuming the main theme, the polars of P_1 for S, S' cut in $P_2(x_2, y_2, z_2)$ where

$$x_2 = (bc' - b'c)y_1z_1, \quad y_2 = (ca' - c'a)z_1x_1, \quad z_2 = (ab' - a'b)x_1y_1.$$

Hence x_1x_2, y_1y_2, z_1z_2 are constants, say k_1, k_2, k_3, independent of the position of P_1.

The transformation from P_1 to P_2 is not a collineation, for it turns the line $lx + my + nz = 0$ into

$k_1l/x + k_2m/y + k_3n/z = 0$, of form $fyz + gzx + hxy = 0$. This is a conic round the triangle of reference*, and by the way it was obtained, it is the locus of the poles of (l, m, n) for the conics $S + kS'$.

In particular, the locus of the centres of conics through four points is a conic; if the points are orthocentric this conic is their nine-point-circle, the conics through the points are rectangular hyperbolas (§ 54).

If we take as reference triangle OIJ with sides $x \pm iy = 0$, $z = 0$, $(x, y, z$ real), the transformation is given by $(x_1 + iy_1)(x_2 + iy_2) = $ const., $(x_1 - iy_1)(x_2 - iy_2) = $ const., $z_1 z_2 = $ const.

If the first two constants are equal, these equations give

$$(x_1^2 + y_1^2)(x_2^2 + y_2^2)/z_1^2 z_2^2 = \text{const.}, \quad x_1/y_1 = -x_2/y_2;$$

which are the Cartesian equations for an inversion, followed by a reflection in the x-axis. A line becomes a conic through I,J, that is, a circle. Our quadratic transformation is a generalization of an inversion.

Dually we have a transformation of a line (l_1, m_1, n_1) into (l_2, m_2, n_2) when l_1l_2, m_1m_2, n_1n_2 are constants.

The envelope of the polars of a given point, for a pencil of conics touching four lines, is a conic.

59. *Some Projective theorems.* (1) If we take the poles with respect to conic S of tangents to conic S_1, their locus is a conic S_2, the *"reciprocal"* of S_1 for S. It is the envelope of polars of points on S_1 with respect to S.

If S, S_1, referred to their common self-polar triangle, have equations

---

* For instance, $x = 1$, $y = 0$, $z = 0$. satisfies the equation.

$Ax^2 + By^2 + Cz^2 = 0$ and $a_1x^2 + b_1y^2 + c_1z^2 = 0$,
the reciprocal mentioned is
$a_2x^2 + b_2y^2 + c_2z^2 = 0$, where $a_1a_2 = A^2, b_1b_2 = B^2, c_1c_2 = C^2$.

Thus any conic can be reciprocated into any other which cuts it in four distinct points, real or not.

(2) The locus of points from which tangents to
$$ax^2 + by^2 + cz^2 = 0 \text{ and } x^2 + y^2 + z^2 = 0$$
separate harmonically, is:
$$a(b + c)x^2 + b(c + a)y^2 + c(a + b)z^2 = 0,$$
the "*harmonic locus*" of the two conics.

(3) Two triangles self-polar for one conic have their vertices on another conic. For take one of the triangles as the reference triangle, and $ax^2 + by^2 + cz^2 = 0$ as the equation of the conic. Let $P_1P_2P_3$ be the other triangle. We have $ax_1x_2 + by_1y_2 + cz_1z_2 = 0$, and similar equations by cycling subscripts 1, 2, 3. These give

$$\begin{vmatrix} 1/x_1, & 1/y_1, & 1/z_1 \\ 1/x_2, & 1/y_2, & 1/z_2 \\ 1/x_3, & 1/y_3, & 1/z_3 \end{vmatrix} = 0$$

Hence there are constants a', b', c' such that P_1, P_2, P_3 all satisfy $a'/x + b'/y + c'/z = 0$, which is the equation of a conic round the reference triangle.

(4) It easily follows that if a conic locus S and a conic envelope Σ be so placed that one triangle in S is self polar for Σ, there is an infinite number of such triangles. Reciprocating [Cf (1)], we find that an infinite number of triangles round Σ are self-polar for S.

Conics like S, Σ are "*apolar*".

(5) If S, Σ are $\quad ax^2 + by^2 + cz^2 + 2fyz + 2gzx + 2hxy = 0$
$\qquad\qquad$ and $\quad Al^2 + Bm^2 + Cn^2 + 2Fmn + 2Gnl + 2Hlm = 0$
the condition for apolarity is
$$aA + bB + cC + 2fF + 2gG + 2hH = 0.$$

From this it follows that if three conic loci be independent, i.e. not in the same pencil, there are three independent envelopes apolar to them.

A degenerate conic envelope, or point-pair, is apolar to a conic locus S when the two points are conjugate for S.

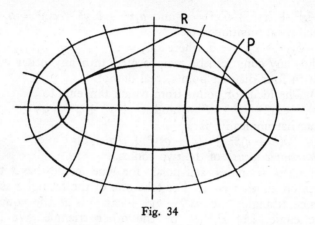

Fig. 34

60. *Some theorems on confocals.* As confocals are a case of conics touching four lines, we have, as cases of theorems of § 58:

The poles of a given line for a set of confocals lie on a line (perpendicular to the given line); the envelope of the polars of a given point is a parabola (Steiner's), touching the principal axes.

Through each point P of the plane, not on a principal axis, go two conics of a given confocal system, an ellipse and a hyperbola, and they meet at right angles. The tangent to the ellipse at P is the locus of the poles, for the system, of the tangent to the hyperbola at P, and vice versa (Fig. 34).

From a given point Q we can draw four normals to an ellipse, and all are real, if Q is inside the envelope in Fig. 32, otherwise two only. The feet of these normals lie on a rectangular hyperbola (Apollonius), which goes through Q and through the centre of the ellipse, and has asymptotes parallel to the principal axes of the

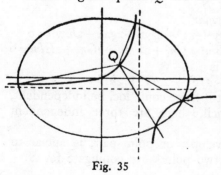

Fig. 35

ellipse. It is the reciprocal, with respect to the ellipse, of the Steiner parabola of Q for the confocal system which contains the ellipse.

A theorem of Poncelet's states that if a variable polygon be drawn round a conic, and all its vertices, save one, are known to describe confocals to the given conic, so does the remaining vertex. There must be a corresponding theorem on conics touching four lines, and as any two general conics are of this kind, we find: if one polygon can be drawn round one given conic and inscribed in another, an infinite number of such polygons can be drawn. For two circles this theorem connects up with Steiner's ring, § 20.

The figure dual to conics touching four lines is one in which conics go through four points; if two of these be I, J we have coaxal circles. Thence, if a variable polygon be inscribed in one circle and all sides, save one, are known to touch circles coaxal with the given, so does the remaining side.

This is connected with the dynamics of pendulum motion. Suppose the pendulum is attached to a light rod, and swings round describing complete circles. If the arcs $P_1 Q_1$, $P_2 Q_2$ . . . are described in equal intervals of time, the chords $P_1 Q_1$, $P_2 Q_2$, . . . will touch a circle. Taking different intervals, we get circles coaxal with that described by the pendulum. This gives an interpretation of the previous theorem.

The theorem on confocals also has an interesting side-line. If a loop of string is slung round a conic, so that part hugs the conic, and the rest is a pair of tangents to the conic from R (Fig. 34), and we put a pencil at R, and move it along, then R describes a confocal. (Graves).

CHAPTER IV

PROJECTIVE GEOMETRY

61. "PROJECTIVE Geometry," said Cayley, "is all Geometry," and though the dictum is too sweeping, it is likely that projective geometry will remain a fundamental discipline for a long time. In the engineering world, it led to the invention of the method of graphical statics.

Projective geometry deals with what may be called the graphical properties of figures, and as far as the plane is concerned, with those properties only which are not changed when we project, in the ordinary sense of the term, from one plane to another; for instance, if we use a source of light, and cast the shadow on to one plane of a figure on the other.

As such a projection usually destroys the congruence of triangles, and changes right angles into angles different from right angles, the relation of congruence and the property of being a right angle are not topics of projective geometry. Similarly a circle is not a figure of projective geometry, for by projection it may become any kind of conic. The property of parallelism for lines, and that expressed by saying that a point is inside a triangle, are not projective properties, because they may be destroyed by projection.

These exclusions leave as the only projective properties in a plane, the collinearity of points, and the concurrence of lines, and it is on this slender basis that we build our theory.

62. *An abstract Science.* We shall treat projective geometry as an abstract deductive science, and we first consider how such a science must be constructed. The following is also relevant to future chapters.

In a deductive science each theorem is deduced from preceding theorems, and, as we must start somewhere, there will be theorems with which we begin; as these will not be proved, they must be assumed. These initial theorems we call *axioms*, and this word is to be understood strictly in the sense stated: an axiom is *merely* an initial unproved theorem. The questions whether it is self-evident or simple are irrelevant.

63. There must be a logic of some kind, anterior to any deductive science, and used in its development. We give a general indication of what we regard as in the province of logic:

First, the notions to which the following words and phrases point; theorem: the assertion that a theorem is true: the conjunction of two theorems (p and q): the disjunction of two theorems (p or q or perhaps both): implication (if p is true, then q is true): inference (p is true, therefore q is true): negation (the contradictory of p).

Secondly, the notions of an *element*, and of a *class* of elements, and of variable elements and classes, and such propositions as "the element a is a member of the class A", "there are members of the class A", "there is just one member of the class A".

Thirdly, we need *relations* between two terms, as in "Abraham begat Isaac", or between three terms such as "Isaac preferred Jacob to Esau", or between four terms such as "the reconciliation between A and B destroyed the concord between C and D".

If we say a set A is transformed into a set B, this is only another way of saying that A, B are *related* in a particular way.

An important relation* is the "*one-to-one correspondence*". Such a correspondence between sets A, B matches each element of A with just one of B, and each element of B with just one of A.

These indications of the logical background must suffice. A full account would more than fill this book.

64. Besides the logical vocabulary, each science has its own words which indicate the elements, classes, relations with which it deals. Some of these are introduced by definitions.

By a "*definition*" we mean only a declaration that we intend

* "Every time," said the tutor to an undergraduate, "I look out of the window, I see you crossing the court." "Every time, Sir," was the reply, "I cross the court, I see you looking out of the window." A one-to-one correspondence.

to replace a long phrase by a shorter. Thus instead of saying "the right-hand side of a ship when we face the direction in which it is sailing", we say "starboard". A definition thus defines a word used in a science by means of words of that science which have been introduced already. We must therefore begin with terms in the science which have not been defined in that science. These we call *"undefined terms"*. They may be of the nature of elements, classes, or relations.

Hence as the basis of a deductive science we have: (1) undefined terms, (2) axioms. An axiom is an unproved theorem which will contain some or all of the undefined terms.

If now we can find elements, classes, and relations outside our science, which when substituted for the undefined terms in our axioms, yield theorems recognized, on grounds outside our science, as true, then all the deductions will be true in the same sense, and we shall have an *interpretation* of our abstract science.

Even when we are working inside the abstract science, it is still a help to have an interpretation in mind, and for this reason figures are often drawn; but if this is done, we must read from them nothing which is not explicitly assumed or deduced in the abstract theory, for the figures are not constituents of the proof but only aids to its comprehension.

65. *Axioms of plane projective geometry.* For undefined terms we take *"point"* and *"line"*. The "points" are the elements we are talking about; a "line" is a special class of these elements. The proposition "the point A is on the line a" thus states that the element A is in the class a.

Our basic Axioms shall be:

Ax. 1. If two distinct points be given, there is just one line on which both lie.

Ax. 2. If two distinct lines be given, there is just one point which lies on both.

(It is obviously enough to assert in Ax. 2 that there is at least one point which lies on both. Its uniqueness then follows from Ax. 1.)

If A, B be distinct points, the line on which both lie is denoted by AB. If a, b be distinct lines, the point which lies on both is denoted by *ab*. Thus the common point of the lines *AB*, *CD* will be denoted by *AB.CD*, the line through the points *ab*, *cd* by *ab.cd*.

In order to avoid cumbrous language, we shall use such common phrases as "the line *AB* goes through *A* and *B*", the "lines *a*, *b* cut in *ab*", and words like "collinear", "concurrent". A set of points on a line may be called a *"range"*, a set of lines through a point *O* a *"pencil"* with *"centre"* *O*.

Since, by Ax. 2, any two lines meet, there is nothing in this theory corresponding to Euclid's parallel lines. This prompts us to ask whether the axioms are consistent, or whether they will eventually yield a contradiction. We shall shew they are consistent by giving an interpretation in which they can be seen to hold:

In a fire-watching scheme it was arranged that any two specified members of the team should be on duty together on one night only, and that only one member should be on duty on both of any two specified nights. Is this possible?

The analogy is clear: replace "member" by "point", and "night" by "line", and "member *A* is on duty at night *a*" by "the point *A* is on the line *a*"; the regulations then become our two axioms.

If we take seven members and seven nights, denoting the members by 1, 2, . . . 7, and the nights by 1′, 2′, . . . 7′, and put in a column under the night, the members on duty that night, the following scheme *A* satisfies the conditions:

A.	1′	2′	3′	4′	5′	6′	7′
	1	2	3	4	5	6	7
	2	3	4	5	6	7	1
	4	5	6	7	1	2	3

B.	1′	2′	. . .	13′
	1	2	. . .	13
	2	3	. . .	1
	4	5	. . .	3
	10	11	. . .	9

Scheme *B* for 13 men and 13 nights also satisfies the conditions.

Such a scheme is called a *"finite projective geometry"*. There are many of these; they have recently been used in designing experiments in agriculture.

Thus our axioms are consistent, at any rate for a finite

number of points. The question for an infinite number is considered later.

To ensure that we have enough points to work with, we assume:

Ax. 3. At least four points, no three of which are collinear, exist.

It then follows that all lines contain at least three points, and that through each point go at least three lines; but scheme A shews that we cannot at present prove there are more than three points on a line, while scheme B shews there could be more without contradiction.

66. *Desargues' theorem.* We shall need only one further major axiom, though we introduce temporarily two, denoted by D and F. The first is Desargues' theorem on perspective triangles, where by a triangle we mean three non-collinear points and the three lines which join them in pairs.

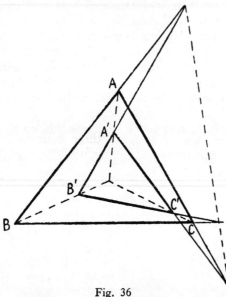

Ax. D. If *ABC*, *A' B' C'* be two triangles, the six sides being distinct, and the six vertices distinct, and if *AA'*, *BB'*, *CC'* concur, then the points *BC.B'C'*, *CA.C'A'*, *AB.A'B'* colline.

The converse easily follows from Axs. 1, 2.

Ax. D is satisfied in certain finite geometries, for example that of scheme B.

Fig. 36

metries, for example that of scheme B.

67. *The principle of duality.* If we examine Axs. 1, 2 we notice that they are related in this way: one is derived from the other when the words "point" and "line" are interchanged

and consequential changes made. Statements so related are called *"dual"*. The dual of D is its converse, which follows from Axs. 1, 2, 3, D. The other assumptions we shall make also have deducible duals.

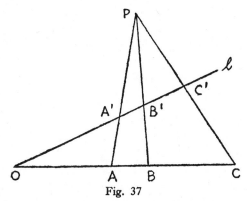

Fig. 37

Now if the axioms become other axioms or deducible theorems when the words "point" and "line" are interchanged and consequential changes made, then if these changes be made in any deduction, we shall have another valid deduction; and if in any true theorem, another true theorem. All the work could be set out in parallel columns of dual statements.

We may avoid this duplication by giving, as a rule, only one of the dual theorems or proofs, though when two dual theorems differ greatly in appearance, we may state both.

A *"quadrilateral"* is a set of four lines, no three concurrent; a *"quadrangle"* is a set of four points, no three collinear.

68. *Projectivities.* We now proceed with technical developments.

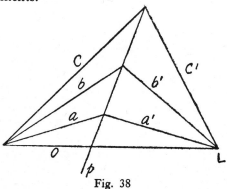

Fig. 38

If $O, A, B, C, \ldots$ be collinear points, and l a line through O, distinct from OA, and P a point on neither line, and if lines PA, PB, $PC, \ldots$ meet l in $A', B', C' \ldots$ then we say that the range of points $ABC \ldots$ is *"perspective"* to the range $A'B'C' \ldots \ldots$

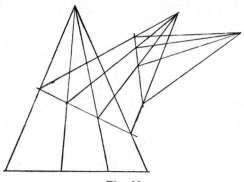

Fig. 39

Dually, if $o, a, b, c, \ldots$ be concurrent lines, and L a point on o distinct from oa, and p a line through neither point, and if points $pa, pb, pc, \ldots$ when joined to L, give lines $a', b', c' \ldots$ then we say that the pencil of lines $abc \ldots$ is *"perspective"* to the pencil $a'b'c' \ldots$.

If we repeat the process, so that $ABC \ldots$ is perspective to $A'B'C' \ldots$, this to $A''B''C'' \ldots$, and so to $A_1B_1C_1 \ldots$, then we say that ranges $ABC \ldots$ and $A_1B_1C_1$ are *"projective"*, or are related by a *"projectivity"*. Similarly for pencils $abc \ldots$ and $a_1b_1c_1 \ldots$.

Any three collinear points can be projected into any other three collinear points. For if A, B, C be on one line, and A_1, B_1, C_1 on another, Fig. 40 shews how we can project A, B, C into A_1, B_1, C_1; if both sets are on the same line, we can project A, B, C to three points on another line, and then these to A_1, B_1, C_1.

Thus if we want to make a statement about points on a line, which is to be characteristic, it must be about four points at least.

69. *Harmonic ranges and pencils.* If four collinear points A, B, C, D be such that we can find a quadrangle $PQRS$ such that $PS.QR = A$, $RS.PQ = C$, and QS goes through B, RP goes through D, then we say A, B, C, D is a *"harmonic range"*, that

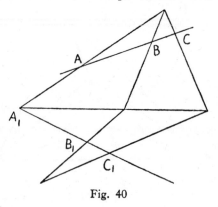

Fig. 40

"*B, D separate A, C har-monically*", and are "*har-monic conjugates*" for A, C.

To make sure that we have enough points for this definition to have meaning, we assume a minor Axiom.

Fano's Axiom. If B, D separate the distinct points A, C harmonically, they are themselves distinct.

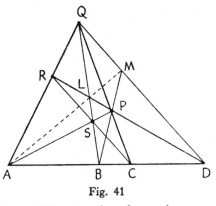

Fig. 41

This Axiom holds in scheme B but not in scheme A.

Our definition of harmonic separation makes this relation depend on the points P, Q, R, S. To shew that it is independent of the choice of these points, we should have to prove that if P', Q', R', S' be any points such that $P'S'.Q'R' = A$, $R'S'.P'Q' = C$, and $Q'S'$ goes through B, then $R'P'$ goes through D.

This can be shewn from D, which also shews that the harmonic conjugate of B for A, C is unique.

It is now of great importance to notice that if B, D separate A, C harmonically, then A, C separate B, D harmonically. For we can construct from Fig. 41 another related to A, C as that one is to B, D. In fact if $M = BP.QD$ and $L = DR.QB$, then from D it follows that A, L, M colline and thus $QLPM$ is a quadrangle of the kind we need.

The dual figure gives the definition of the property: the lines b, d separate a, c harmonically.

Here a, b, c, d are so placed that we can find a

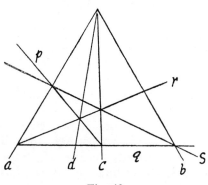

Fig. 42

quadrilateral *pqrs* such that $ps.qr = a$, $rs.pq = c$, qs is on b, rp is on d.

The proof dual to the last shews that then a, c separate b, d harmonically.

If we compare Figs. 41 and 42 we have at once: If points A, B, C, D of a harmonic range be joined to any point not on this line, the joins form a harmonic pencil; and a harmonic pencil is cut by any line, not through its centre, in a harmonic range.

Thus the projection of a harmonic range is a harmonic range; of a harmonic pencil, a harmonic pencil. Thus in Fig. 41, QA, QB, QC, QD cut DS in a harmonic range.

70. *The Fundamental Theorem.* We have seen that, whereas *any* three collinear points can be projected into *any* other three such points, four points of a harmonic range can only be projected into four harmonic points; they cannot be projected into four arbitrary collinear points.

This raises the question how far a projectivity between two ranges of points is fixed. If by some sequence of perspectivities we transform the collinear points A, B, C, D into the collinear points A_1, B_1, C_1, D_1, it by no means follows from our assumptions that another sequence of perspectivities which turns A, B, C into A_1, B_1, C_1 will necessarily turn D into D_1.

This is what we now virtually affirm in our Fundamental theorem:

Ax. F. If by a projectivity, each of three collinear points is transformed into itself, so is every point of their line.

Whence if one projectivity turned A, B, C, D into A_1, B_1, C_1, D_1, and another turned them into A_1, B_1, C_1, D'_1 the reverse of the first, followed by the second would turn A_1, B_1, C_1, D_1 into A_1, B_1, C_1, D'_1 and hence $D_1 = D'_1$.

Thus if a range of points is projected into another range, the fate of any point is determined when the fates of three are known. The following is a very important consequence :

Suppose the range $OABC$... on one line is projective to $OA'B'C'$... on another, O being *self-corresponding*, then if AA', BB' meet in X, the perspectivity, centre X, turns O, A, B into O, A',B'. The fates of the three points O, A, B are the same under the perspectivity as under the projectivity.

Hence by Ax. F
these transform-
ations coincide:
AA', BB', CC',
... concur.

71. *Ax.* P
Pappus' theorem.
If A, B, C be
collinear points,
and A', B', C'
points on an-
other line, then
the cuts BC'.
$B'C$, $CA'.C'A$,
$AB'.A'B$ are collinear.

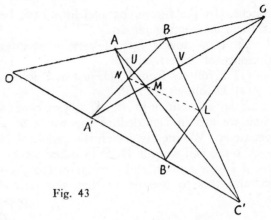

Fig. 43

We can prove this if we assume F. For let L, M, N be the
cuts mentioned, and let $U = AC'.A'B$, $V=CA'.\ BC'$,
$O = AB.A'B'$. Then O, A', B', C' project from A to B, A',
$N U$ on $A'B$, and also project from C to B, V, L, C' on BC'.

Hence B, A', N, U and B, V, L, C' are projective, with
B as self-corresponding point. Hence by the previous section,
$A'V$, NL, UC' concur, which is equivalent to the statement.

72. The duals of F and P can be shewn from Axs. 1, 2, 3, F.
The first is: if a pencil of lines be projective to another
pencil, and the
fates of three lines
be known, the
fate of any line
of the pencil is
determined.

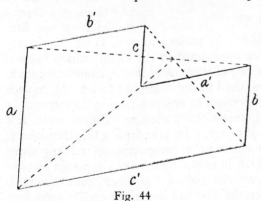

Fig. 44

Dual of P. If
a, b, c be three
lines of one pencil,
and a', b', c' three
of another, then
the joins $bc'.b'c$,
$ca'.c'a$, $ab'.a'b$

concur. (In the figure, parallel lines have been drawn; think of them as meeting far away.)

73. It is now a fact of very great interest that, in the presence of Axs. 1, 2, 3:

(1) F follows from P, D, just as P followed from F.

(2) D follows from P.

Hence in addition to Axs. 1, 2, 3 *we need assume* P *only*, and then we can in fact deduce the whole of projective (plane) geometry. We merely sketch the proofs of (1) and (2).

To see (1), we put D, P in other forms: D is equivalent to: if l, m, n concur, and a range on l is perspective to one on m, and this to one on n, then the ranges on l, n are in perspective.

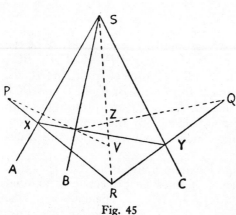

Fig. 45

As for P, we refer to Fig. 43 and restate: If $A'BC'$ be a triangle, and A, B, C be collinear, the result of projecting a range on $A'B$ from A into one on $A'C'$, and then from C into one on BC'' is a perspectivity, with centre M.

Now F refers to any chain of perspectivities from one line back to the line, and by the present form of D we can replace any three consecutive lines, used in the chain, which happen to be concurrent, by two of them. And if a, b, c be consecutive, non-concurrent lines, used in the chain, we can, by D, replace b by any line b' not through ac and not joining corresponding points on a, c, and do this without affecting the final result. If d is the line next used after a, b, c, we take for b' a line through cd, thus obtaining two consecutive perspectivities relating three concurrent lines, which lines can therefore be replaced by two.

So proceeding, we can reduce the figure, until there is only one line between the first and last in the chain; according as these three concur or not, we find that F is equivalent to D or to P as formulated in this section.

To shew (2): Let ranges on SA, SB be perspective from P, and ranges on SB, SC perspective from Q. If we call these perspectivities T_1, T_2, then D is equivalent to the statement that T_1T_2 is a perspectivity. Let X, Y be on SA, SC but be not corresponding points, and let P, Q be not on their join. We repeatedly use P as formulated in this section.

Let $R = PX.QY$, and let T be the perspectivity, centre R, which turns SB into XY, and T^{-1} be its inverse. Then, by P, T_1T is a perspectivity with its centre V on SR, which turns SA into XY, and $T^{-1}T_2$ is a perspectivity with its centre Z in SR, which turns XY into SC.

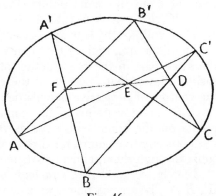

Fig. 46

Hence, again by P, as T_1T, $T^{-1}T_2$ have their centres on SR, their product is a perspectivity which turns SA into SC. But this product is T_1T_2. Hence D is proved.

74. We have spent so much time on the foundations, to shew the reader the type of argument to be used, so that he may appreciate the generality of the theory and the slender basis on which it is built. We do not care whether a line contains a finite or an infinite number of points, and yet from our assumptions we can deduce a theory of conics, cubic curves, and so on.

75. *Conics* will now be defined from our present point of view.

For two perspective pencils with distinct centres, the cuts of corresponding lines are collinear, by definition.

If two pencils are projective, but not perspective, the locus of cuts of corresponding lines is called a *"conic"*.

If A, C be the centres of the pencils, some line of the

second pencil corresponds to AC in the first; these corresponding lines meet in C; hence C, and similarly A, are on the conic.

If three other points A', B', C' be given (and no three of the five colline), then the projectivity is determined when AA', AB', AC' correspond to CA', CB', CC'. Thus just one conic can be drawn through the five points, but we must note that the five do not enter in the same way: two centres, three given points.

By an argument like that which proved Pappus' theorem, we can shew that if B is another point on the conic, such that the set of joins of A to A', B', C', B is projective to the set of joins of C to the same points, then D, E, F colline, where $D = BC'.B'C$, $E = CA'.C'A$, $F = AB'.A'B$. Conversely if D, E, F colline, the sets are projective (Fig. 46).

In this figure, each of the points A, B, C, A', B', C' plays the same part in the construction of the line DEF; whence it easily follows, that any two of these points could be taken as the centres of projective pencils defining the same conic, and, since B was any point on the conic, it follows that any two points on the conic will serve as the centres of the pencils.

Thus any five points, no three collinear, determine just one conic through them, and any five points on it fix the same conic.

Finally we get *Pascal's famous theorem* (1639); If A, B, C, A', B', C' be any six points on a conic, then the cuts $BC'.B'C$, $CA'.C'A$, $AB'.A'B$ are collinear.

It is sometimes convenient to extend the definition of a conic to include "degenerate" conics, made up of line-pairs. If the pencils with centres A, C are perspective, one line of the pair is the locus of cuts of corresponding lines of the pencil, the other is AC.

76. *Tangents.* It is easily proved by reductio ad absurdum that the line of the pencil, centre C, which corresponds to the line AC of the pencil, centre A, does not meet the curve at any point other than C. We call this line the "*tangent*" to the conic at C. Since C may be any point on the conic, we thus have without any continuity assumptions: at each point of the conic there is just one tangent.

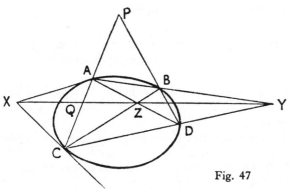

Fig. 47

77. Poles and polars. If A, B, C, D be four points on the conic, consider the six lines: the tangent at A, AB, BC, the tangent at C, CD, DA.

Without continuity assumptions, using reductio ad absurdum, it can be shewn that Pascal's theorem applies here also. Accordingly, if the tangents at A, C meet in X, and if $AB.CD = Y$, $BC.AD = Z$, then X, Y, Z colline. Further, if $AC.BD = P$, $AC.YZ = Q$ then P, Q are harmonic conjugates of A, C, by the definition of harmonic ranges.

Keep the line PAC fixed, and let PBD vary, always passing through the fixed point P, then X, Q and hence the line XQ are fixed. This line, by the argument above, goes through the cut of tangents at B, D, and through the harmonic conjugate of P for B, D.

Hence if P is any point not on the conic, and lines be drawn through it to cut the conic, the tangents at the cuts meet on a fixed line, which goes through the harmonic conjugates of P for the cuts.

This line is the "*polar*" of P (§ 47), and P is its "*pole*".

If P is on the conic, its polar is defined to be the tangent at P. Note that PXZ is a self-polar triangle (Cf. § 49).

78. *Conic envelopes.* We ought now to dualize all the

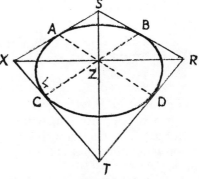

Fig. 48

above. The dual of a conic locus is a "*conic envelope*" defined thus:

If we have two ranges of points, projective but not perspective, on two distinct lines, the envelope of joins of corresponding points is a conic envelope.

The reader will expect that the tangents to a conic locus yield a conic envelope. The theorem is not trivial; the corresponding one for cubic curves would be false.

To prove the theorem, draw the tangents at B, D in the last figure. By what we proved in § 77, these meet on XZ. Similarly, if S, T be their cuts with the tangents from X, then S, T, Z colline.

Now let AX, XT, TD be fixed tangents, and SR a variable tangent. Then Z varies on the fixed line AD, describing a range perspective from T to the range of S, and perspective from X to the range of R. Hence S, R describe projective ranges, and the join SR envelops a conic envelope, viz. the original conic.

79. We can now deduce the dual of Pascal's theorem:—

Brianchon's theorem. If a, b, c, a', b', c' be tangents to a conic (locus or envelope), the joins $bc'.b'c$, $ca'.c'a$, $ab'.a'b$ meet in a point.

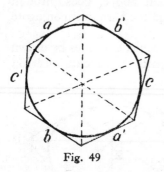

Fig. 49

80. *Involution.* If a range of points on a line is projected back to the line by a series of perspectivities, a point A of the line becomes, say, A'. If by a repetition of the perspectivities, A' becomes A'', then, as a rule, A, A'' are distinct. But if they coincide, we shall shew that, if B be *any* point of the line which becomes in succession B', B'', then B'' coincides with B.

For, first, if A, A', B, B' be any collinear points, there is always a projectivity which interchanges A and A', and also B and B'. For take any line u through A, and any point S not on u or AB. Let u cut SA', SB, SB' in X, Y, Z; let $B'Y$ cut SA' in C.

Projecting in turn from S, B', Y we see that the ranges

$AA'BB'$, $AXYZ$, $A'XCS$, $A'AB'B$ are projective.

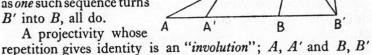

Fig. 50

Now if *any* sequence of perspectivities turned A, A', B into A', A, B', the fate, under the sequence, of the point B', regarded as in the first range, is determined, and as *one* such sequence turns B' into B, all do.

A projectivity whose repetition gives identity is an *"involution"*; A, A' and B, B' are "pairs" in the involution above.

We also say *A corresponds to A'*. An involution may have two self-corresponding parts X, Y. Then these separate any pair A, A' harmonically.

Dually we can define a *"pencil in involution"*. Any line cuts it in a range in involution.

81. The most important theorem on involutions is *Desargues' theorem*. The set of conics through four points cut any line in pairs of an involution. The tangents from a given point to conics touching four lines are pairs of a pencil in involution.

If P describes a line l, its polar p for a conic describes a pencil of lines through L, the pole of l. The lines p cut l in points P', such that P, P' are pairs in an involution.

82. *Ranges on a conic.* If a point P be taken *on* a conic, we can project a range in a line, on to the conic, from P, by joining P to a point A_1 of the range, and taking the cut A of PA_1 and the conic.

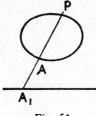

Fig. 51

If in this way we project two projective ranges, or a range in involution on a line, on to a conic, we say we have two *"projective ranges"*, or a *"range in involution"* on the conic. If these ranges on the conic be joined to *any* point *on* the conic we have two projective pencils of lines, or a pencil of lines in involution, respectively. Similarly a harmonic range on a line is projected into a *"harmonic range"* on the conic; if it be joined to *any* point *on* the conic we get a harmonic pencil.

The main theorem on projective ranges on a conic is an extension of Pascal's theorem: the *criss-cross theorem*:

If A, B, C, ... X, Y ... and A', B', C', ..., X', Y' ... be projective ranges on a conic the cuts of the cross joins $AB'.A'B$, ..., $XY'.X'Y$, ... lie on a line, the *"axis"* of the projectivity.

The joins of corresponding points AA', BB', envelope a conic touching the given conic where it cuts the axis of the projectivity, if these cuts exist.

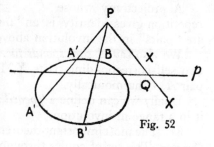

Fig. 52

83. For an involution we have a simpler case: if A, A', B, B', ... be pairs in involution on the conic, then it can be proved that AA', BB' ... concur in P, say, the *"vertex"* of the involution.

Suppose p is the polar of P, and regard the involution as a transformation interchanging A with A'; B with B'. ...

If X is any point in the plane and PX cuts p in Q and X' is the harmonic conjugate of X for P, Q, the transformation which changes X into X', and hence X' into X is a *"harmonic homology"* and it is obviously an extension of the involution transformation on the conic.

84. *Products of involutions.* Any projectivity T on a line is the product of two involutions. For suppose it turns A, B, C into A', B', C', and let I_1 be the involution which interchanges A', B and also, B', A, and suppose it turns C into D. Let I_2 be the involution which turns A', B', D into B', A', C', then T = $I_1 I_2$.

The same theorem is, of course, true for a projectivity on a conic, a little more picturesquely. The vertex of the involution I_1 is then $AB'.A'B$, that of I_2 is $A'B'.C'D$. Both these points lie on the axis of the projectivity, and by the criss-cross theorem, we can take for either vertex any point on the axis, which is not also on the conic; the other vertex is then fixed.

Pascal's theorem shews that if I_1, I_2, I_3 are involutions with collinear vertices, then $(I_1I_2I_3)^2 = I$.

If I_1, I_2, I_3 have vertices at the vertices of a self-polar triangle, then

$$I_2I_3 = I_3I_2 = I_1, \qquad I_3I_1 = I_1I_3 = I_2, \qquad I_1I_2 = I_2I_1 = I_3,$$
$$I_1^2 = I_2^2 = I_3^2 = I_1I_2I_3 = I.$$

85. *Consistency*. We emphasize again the great generality of our theory: although we have drawn continuous figures to assist the understanding, our plane might contain only a finite number of points. All the arguments are still valid.

Our theory also includes the case when the number of points is infinite. For consider a co-ordinate geometry in which a point is represented by the ratios of three numbers, not all zero, and a line by a linear equation. Our first two axioms are now simple facts on linear equations, and D, P can be verified by calculation. Hence if this ordinary algebra is consistent so is our geometry, even when the number of points is infinite.

Further, in dealing with linear equations, it matters not whether our numbers are real or complex, and our projective geometry can be regarded as corresponding to the co-ordinate geometry either with real or with complex numbers as basis.

We must, however, make a distinction when we consider the cut of a line and a conic. If we assume they *always* cut, we have the analogue of co-ordinate geometry with complex, but not with real, co-ordinates.

86. *Parallel lines*. We may compare Euclidean geometry, with our projective geometry. We begin with parallels.

Select *once for all* a line in the plane and *call* it "the line at infinity"; two lines which meet on it we will *call* "parallel". Then by Ax. 1, 2; just one parallel goes through a given point to a given line.

If AB meets the line at infinity in C, the harmonic conjugate of C for A, B will be called the *"mid-point"* of AB.

We now easily get a series of statements and definitions which are verbally the same as those of Euclidean geometry.

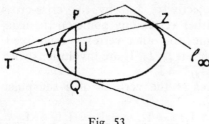

Fig. 53

If in Fig. 41 QD is the line at infinity, then $ACPR$ is a "parallelogram", and its diagonals meet in their mid-points.

The *"centre"* of a conic is the pole of the line at infinity. If the conic does not touch this line, we have from the definition of pole and polar, that the centre is the mid-point of all chords of the conic. If O is the centre of a conic, and the lines l, m through O, together with the line at infinity constitute a self polar triangle for the conic, then l, m are *"conjugate"* diameters, i.e. each bisects all chords parallel to the other.

A conic which touches the line at infinity, at Z, say, we call a "parabola". The lines through Z are its (parallel) "diameters". If P, Q are points of contact of tangents from T, and TZ cuts the parabola in V, and PQ, in U, then V is the mid-point of TU, since T, V, U, Z is a harmonic range. Similarly U is the mid-point of PQ.

87. *Co-ordinates on a line.* We now shew a most astonishing fact. Although we have as yet no "distance", we can introduce co-ordinates. We do this in the first instance by making the points themselves play the part of co-ordinates.

Take a fixed line and on it two points O, U; it will be convenient if U is on the line l, at infinity, chosen above. On l take any point P; through U draw any line m. Then if A, B be any points, *not* U, on OU, we construct a point C as follows. $X = OP.m$, $Q = AX.l$, $Y = PB.m$, $C = QY.OU$.

It can be shewn from D, that C is independent of P, m, l (through U), and depends only on O, U and A, B.

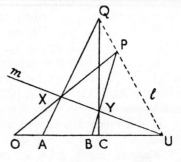

Fig. 54

We keep O, U fixed, and write $A + B = C$, and speak of "*addition*".

This definition and notation would be rather pointless unless the formal algebraical laws held. In fact, we can deduce from D:
$$A + B = B + A, \quad A + (B + C) = (A + B) + C,$$
$$A + O = O + A = A.$$
If A, $B \neq U$, there is a unique point C such that
$$A + C = C + A = B.$$
Thus O plays the part of zero, and we can define subtraction.

Take another fixed point I on OU, and any line n through O still keeping a line l through U, and a point P on it.

Perform the following construction: $X = PI.n$, $Q = AX.l$, $Y = PB.n$, $F = QY.OU$. We can shew again from

Fig. 55

D that the point F depends only on O, U, I and A, B, and is independent of l, n, P.

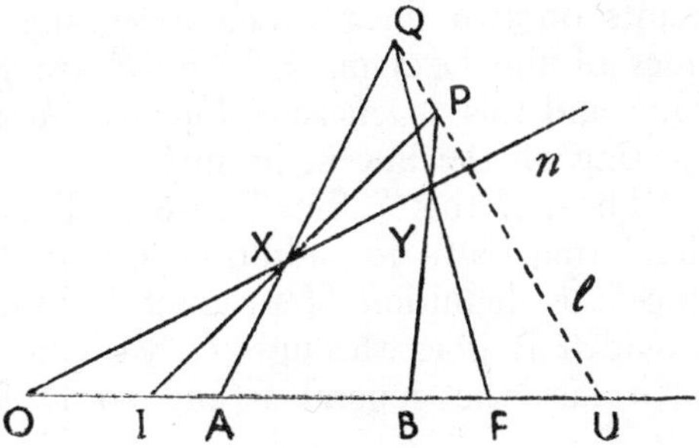

We write: $F = A.B$, and speak of "*multiplication*".

From D we can shew: $A.(B.C.) = (A.B).C$,
$A.(B + C) = A.B + A.C$, $\quad (B + C).A = B.A + C.A$,
$A.I = I.A = A$, $\qquad\qquad A.O = O.A = O$.

If A, $B \neq U$ and $A \neq O$, there is a unique point R such that $A.R = B$, and a unique point L such that $L.A = B$.

Thus I plays the part of unity in multiplication.

The reader will note that all the ordinary formal algebraical laws have been listed above as deducible from D, except $A.B = B.A$.

88. *Pappus' theorem and $A.B = B.A$.* The definitions of $A + B$ and $A.B$ become more vivid, if we draw lines which meet on l to look like parallel lines. We do this and call them parallel.

Thus we have lines OI, OX; A, B on OI. To construct $A.B$, we draw BY parallel to IX to meet OX in Y, and then

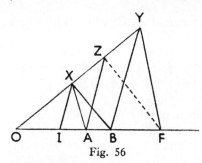

Fig. 56

YF parallel to *XA* to meet *OI* in *F*. Then *F* = *A.B*.

To construct *B.A*, we draw *AZ* parallel to *IX* to meet *OX* in *Z*, and then *ZF'* parallel to *XB* to meet *OI* in *F'*. Then *F'* = *B.A*.

Thus *A.B* = *B.A* is equivalent to:—if *A*, *B*, *F* and *X*, *Y*, *Z* are triads of points on two lines which meet, and two pairs of opposite sides of the hexagon *ZAXBYF* are parallel, so is the third pair; and this is merely *Pappus' theorem*, the opposite sides meeting on the line at infinity.

Thus, if this "affine" case of P is assumed, we have all the formal laws for addition and multiplication, and hence, since the definition of product is independent of the line *l*, provided it goes through *U*, we can deduce P for any such *l*. In fact the general P and so D follow from this affine case.

89. *Field and quasi-field*. A set of elements which satisfy the formal laws above is called a *"field"*; if the commutative law of multiplication is omitted, a *"quasi-field"*. Herein *O*, *I* play the part of 0, 1 and we now denote them by these symbols, and the other elements by small letters, and say now that the points of the line are *represented* by the elements of the field or quasi-field.

90. *Co-ordinates in a plane*. Take any triangle *OUU'* in the plane and points *I*, *I'* on *OU*, *OU'* distinct from *O*, *U*, *U'*, as unit points, i.e. as points which correspond to 1. Put points on *OU*, and on *OU'*, into correspondence with the elements of a quasi-field. If *P* is any point not on *UU'*, and *U'P*, *UP* cut *OU*, *OU'* in *A*, *A'* respectively, and if *x*, *y* are elements of the quasi-field which correspond to *A*, *A'* we say (*x,y*)

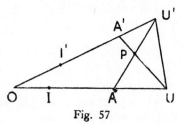

Fig. 57

are the "*co-ordinates*" of P. Points on OU have the second co-ordinate zero, those on OU' the first.

With these co-ordinates, the equation of any line, except UU', can be shown to have the form $ax + by + c = 0$, but unless we assume P as we now shall, we cannot write it also as $xa + yb + c = 0$. UU' is the line at infinity.

We now have contact with Chap. III; we may introduce homogeneous co-ordinates, replacing x, y by x/z, y/z where z is an element of our field, and ascribe to UU' the equation $z = 0$.

A projective transformation along OU is of form

$$x' = (ax + b)/(cx + d), \text{ where } ad - bc \neq 0,$$

and a, b, c, d, are elements of our field. In homogeneous co-ordinates it is written

$$x' = ax + bz, \quad z' = cx + dz.$$

A (non-degenerate) collineation is of form

$$x' = a_1x + b_1y + c_1z, \quad y' = a_2x + b_2y + c_2z,$$
$$z' = a_3x + b_3y + c_3z$$

where the determinant of the coefficients of x, y, z is not zero. If $L = 0$, $M = 0$ are equations of lines, then the equation $L + kM = 0$, as k changes, represents a pencil of lines through the cut of L, M. If by a collineation, L, M become L', M', we can adjust the arbitrary factor in the last expressions, so that $L + kM$ becomes $L' + kM'$. The locus of the cuts of corresponding lines of the two projective pencils, $L + kM = 0$ and $L' + kM' = 0$, is found by eliminating k to be $LM' - L'M = 0$, which is thus the equation of a conic.

The equation of conic is hence of the second degree, as in Chap. II, III.

91. *Euclidean Geometry.* The easiest way to construct a model of this geometry would be to *define* the distance between (x_1, y_1) and (x_2, y_2) to be the square root of $(x_1 - x_2)^2 + (y_1 - y_2)^2$. But we do not know whether elements of our field have square roots; and if we want ordinary Euclidean geometry, it is only elements *greater than* 0 which should have

square roots, and the relation "greater than" is not yet in our system.

Another way would be to define the model of a right angle (Cf § 56). Take an involution on the line at infinity, and define two lines (other than the line at infinity), to be *"perpendicular"* when they meet the line at infinity in a point-pair of the involution.

If P, Q be a pair of the involution, O not on the line at infinity, consider the harmonic homology (§ 83) with vertex P, axis OQ. If A, B correspond in this homology, then P, A, B are on a line perpendicular to OQ, and the homology corresponds to a line reflection of Chap. I, and if we define a *"displacement"* as the product of two such homologies, we can repeat the theory of congruence of that chapter.

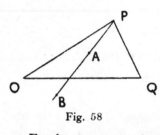

Fig. 58

But there is a snag. Suppose our involution had self-corresponding points; the join of O to such a point would be perpendicular to itself; it would be like the isotropic lines of Chap. III. Thus our geometry might correspond either to the geometry with real co-ordinates or to that with complex co-ordinates.

Furthermore we shall see later that the most important relations in Euclidean geometry are the *order relations*, and these have at present no place.

92. *Finite fields.* If we introduce co-ordinates in a finite projective geometry, these must be elements of a field containing only a finite number of elements. A simple instance of such a field is furnished by integers, mod 7 (or any prime); we get this field if we add and multiply integers, always casting out 7, so that e.g.: $5 + 3 = 1$, $5.4 = 6$. There are also other types of finite fields.

It is highly remarkable that a finite quasi-field is necessarily a field (Wedderburn). Hence if we assume Axs. 1, 2, 3 and D and that the number of points is finite, P follows.

But if the number of elements is not finite, we can construct quasi-fields which are not fields; hence if the number of points in our geometry is infinite, we cannot deduce* P from D, and Axs. 1, 2, 3. In any case we cannot deduce D from Axs. 1, 2, 3.

93. *Higher Dimensions.* To get more than two dimensions it is only necessary to assume:

If *A*, *B*, *C* are non-collinear points, there is a point not on the plane *ABC*.

By *"plane" ABC* we mean the set of all points on all lines joining *A* to points of *BC*. We assume Ax. 2 for lines in a plane, and Ax. 1 for all pairs of points.

If we wish to have three dimensions *only*, we assume that two planes always meet in a *line*.

If we have at least three dimensions we *can* deduce D from axioms 1, 2, but however many dimensions we have, P does *not* follow.

Co-ordinates can be introduced in three dimensions using a tetrahedron instead of a triangle.

In projective space of three dimensions, the point and the plane are dual elements, and the line is a self-dual element. If in any true theorem or valid proof, we interchange the words "point" and "plane" and make consequential changes, (*e.g.* replace the phrase "the points lie on a line by the phrase "the planes go through a line"), then the theorem remains true, and the proof valid.

When we speak of "projective axioms" we do not include Ax. P, (Pappus' Theorem) unless it is explicitly mentioned.

93*a*. If any two non-degenerate conics be given, each can be transformed into the other by a collineation. We say the conics are *"projectively equivalent"*. If one has any property which is unchanged by a collineation, the other also has that property. It is such properties which we considered in §§ 65-90.

---

* Throughout this book "we cannot deduce" means "we can prove we cannot deduce."

CHAPTER V

NON-EUCLIDEAN GEOMETRY

94. *THE Problem.* The usual treatment of elementary geometry in schools now begins with a study of congruent triangles and parallel lines, based on principles derived from drawings and spatial intuition. In earlier days, the ancient text-book of Euclid was used; this attempted a logical treatment of geometrical theory, starting from axioms and definitions, and the first book begins with a theory of congruent triangles which does not use any proposition on parallel lines. About half-way through this book, Euclid began to discuss parallels, and he found it necessary to introduce an axiom he had not previously used. His own formulation has only an historical interest, and we shall use an equivalent form, and call it the *Euclidean parallel axiom*:

Not more than one line can be drawn through a given point parallel to a given line.

Two lines are called "*parallel*" when they lie in the same plane and do not meet. (With us moderns, of course, though not with Euclid, the "line" means the *infinite* straight line.)

It is possible to prove from congruence theory that there is at least one parallel to a given line through a given point. The new assumption is therefore tantamount to a statement that there is *just one*. The isolation of the new assumption and the treatment of congruence without its use, is a remarkable example of the logical capacity of the Greeks, and it suggested attempts in antiquity and in modern times to demonstrate the parallel axiom from the properties of congruent triangles.

All these attempts failed. Those which satisfied their authors were all vitiated by some assumption, often hard to disentangle, equivalent to the theorem to be proved. Let the reader draw intervals *AB*, *BC*, *CD*, *DE*, *EF* in spiral formation, each perpendicular to the preceding. Lobatchefsky, before he attained enlightenment, thought he could prove that the line

80

EF must cut either *AB*, or *BC*, and from this he was able to shew correctly the Euclidean Axiom; but his proof of his lemma was necessarily faulty.

Bolyai and Lobatchefsky independently settled the whole question round about 1830. They assumed the contradictory of the Euclidean axiom: they assumed that through a given point *more than one* (straight) line could go which did not meet a given line, through lying in the same plane with it. If this assumption together with the theorems on congruence leads to a contradiction, we shall have a proof of Euclid's axiom; but if, as is the case, no contradiction can arise, then the new axiom, as well as the Euclidean, leads to a self consistent geometry, not contradicting itself though not agreeing with the Euclidean geometry.

95. *Deductions from the new axiom.* The question of consistency is taken up later, and the reader may for the present suspend his judgment on that point, in following the deductions.

We assume all the Euclidean theorems on congruent triangles, but in place of the Euclidean parallel axiom, the following:

Ax.H. If *P* is a point not on the line *AB*, there are two rays (half-lines) *PX*, *PY* from *P*, not in the same line and not meeting *AB*, and such that any ray *PZ* from *P* inside the angle *XPY* meets *AB* (Fig. 59).

By line we always mean straight line; we emphasize this, because in our figures they may be represented by curved lines. Figures, however, merely illustrate proofs, they are not constituents of proofs; the proof of a theorem in ordinary geometry about a square is not invalidated if the accompanying diagram is not an exact square.

The geometry in which Ax.H holds is called *"hyperbolic geometry"*.

It can now be proved that none of the lines through *P* which pass inside an angle *YPR* adjacent to *YPX* meet *AB*; if we continue to call such lines "parallels", we must say that an *infinite* number of parallels can be drawn through *P* to *AB*.

If *PQ* be perpendicular to *AB*, it is easy to prove that the angles *QPX*, *QPY* are equal. For if *QPX* were the smaller,

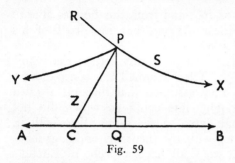

Fig. 59

and we make angle QPZ equal to it, then PZ would cut AB in C, say, and reflection in PQ, which merely involves congruence, would lead to a contradiction.

The angle QPX is called the *"angle of parallelism"* at P, for AB. In Euclid's case it is always a right angle.

We need a word for the rays PX, PY. In non-Euclidean geometries the word "parallel" is often restricted to these, but as we shall continue to use it in its old sense of coplanar and non cutting, we will call PX the *"right ray"*, PY the *"left ray"*, and both *"limit rays"* for the line AB and the point P.

If S is any point on the line PX, through S will go a left ray and a right ray limit rays to AB, and it is easy to prove that the right ray coincides with SX. Thus PX is a right ray at all its points.

Other simple properties are: (1) If PX is a limit ray for QB, so is QB for PX; i.e. all rays through Q in the angle PQB meet PX. (2) if a is a right limit ray for b, and b for c, then so is a for c; similarly for left rays.

These are the symmetric and transitive properties of limit rays. Thus given a ray, we have a whole *"pencil"* of rays each the right ray of each.

96. *Limit triangles.* Suppose PC is a limit ray to AB, produce AP to Q. Then angle QPC is greater than QAB, for if it were less, and we drew PD on the same side of AP as AB so that angle QPD equalled PAB; then PD, falling inside angle APC, would meet AB, in E, say, and we should have a triangle EAP in which

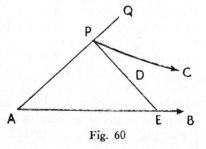

Fig. 60

the exterior angle *QPE* equalled the interior opposite angle *QAE*.

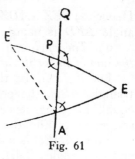

Fig. 61

But this is impossible, both in the Euclidean and in the hyperbolic geometry, as we can see using congruence only: produce *EP* to *E'* so that *PE' = AE*; the congruence of triangles *EAP, E'PA* then proves that angle *PAE' = APE*, and hence *EA, AE'* are in line.

Thus the lines *EP, EA* would meet in *two* points.

If we say the interval *PA* and the rays *AB, PC* in Fig. 60 constitute a "*limit triangle*", we have the result that the exterior angle of such a triangle is greater than an interior opposite angle.

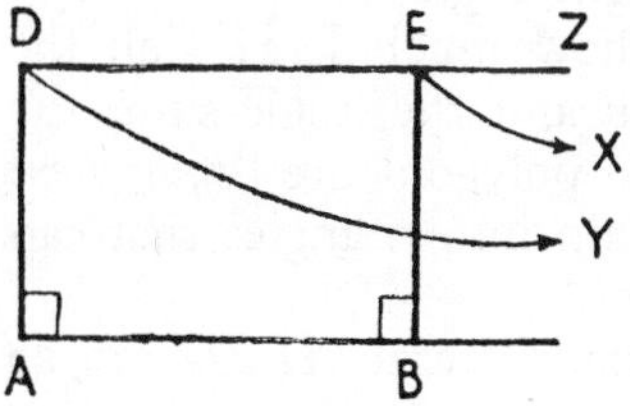

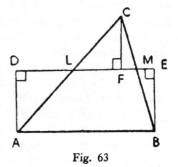

Fig. 62

97. It can now be proved that if we have two limit triangles, one constituted by the interval *PA* and the rays *AB, PC*, and the other similarly by *P'A', A'B', P'C'*, then:

If *PA = P'A'* and angle *A = A'*, then angle *P = P'*.

If angle *A = A'* and angle *P = P'*, then *PA = P'A'*. In particular, the angle of parallelism at *P* depends only on the distance from *P* to *AB*, and (§ 96), it decreases as *PQ* increases.

98. *Saccheri's quadrilateral* (1733). In this quadrilateral *ABED*, the angles at *A, B* are right angles and *AD = BE*.

If the angles at *D, E* were also right angles, we should have Euclid's case. We prove that here they are *acute* (Fig. 62):

Produce *DE* to *Z*, and draw the right rays *DY, EX* from *D, E* to *AB*.

Then by § 96, $\angle ZEX > ZDY$, and by § 97, $\angle BEX = ADY$.

Fig. 63

Hence $\angle BEZ > ADZ$. But $\angle ADZ = BED$. Hence the angle BED is acute.

99. *The angle-sum of a triangle.* We can now shew that *the sum of the angles of any triangle is less than two right angles.*

For if L, M be the mid-points of the sides CA, CB of triangle ABC, the perpendiculars AD, BE, CF on LM are equal, by congruence of triangles. (We must not use any properties of Euclidean parallels.) (Fig. 63.)

Thus $ADEB$ is a Saccheri quadrilateral head downwards, and thus angles DAB, EBA are acute, but (congruence again) the first is the sum of angles LCF, LAB, and the second of angles MCF, MBA, and the total sum of these four is the sum of the angles of triangle ABC, which, as it equals the sum of two acute angles, is less than two right angles.

The reader will naturally ask, how much less? Call the difference between two right angles and the angle-sum, the *"defect"* of the triangle; and say two polygons are *"equivalent by addition"* when one can be split up into triangles that can be fitted together to make the other.

Thus triangle ABC and the quadrilateral $ABED$ are so related. It is now possible to show that triangles equivalent by addition have the same defect, for if a triangle be split into two, the defect of the whole is the sum of the defects of the parts.

This suggests, and it is true, that the defect of a triangle can be taken as a measure of its area.

In particular, if a triangle is small, its angle-sum is nearly two right angles, and the geometry is "nearly" Euclidean inside the triangle. But what does "small" mean? It must mean small compared with some intrinsic length in the space. We take this up later.

100. *Pencils of lines.* So far we have had two kinds of relations between a pair of lines; (1) they may cut, (2) there may be rays, one on each, which are limit rays of each other.

There is only one other possibility; two lines may have just one common perpendicular line; if two lines had two common perpendiculars, we could deduce the Euclidean axiom.

To shew that a pair of lines, not of the kind (1) or (2) have a common perpendicular, we follow Hilbert (1899). Drop a pair of perpendiculars AP, BQ from points A, B on one line to the other. If $AP = BQ$ the line mid-way between the lines AP, BQ is the common perpendicular. If AP is the greater, let

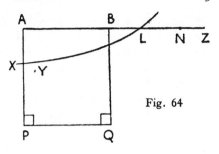

Fig. 64

$PX = QB$, produce AB to Z, make angle $PXY = QBZ$. It can be proved that the line XY meets AZ, in L say. Cut off BN along BZ equal to XL.

Then the perpendiculars from L, N to PQ are equal, and the line mid-way between them is the required common perpendicular.

101. Because of the existence of three types of "pencils" (1) lines meeting in a point, (2) lines whose right rays (or whose left rays) are limit rays of each other, (3) lines with a common perpendicular, some theorems in Euclidean geometry now take strange forms:

The right bisectors of the sides of a triangle, the three altitudes of a triangle, may each be three lines of a pencil of any of these kinds.

Thus if we attempt to find the centre of a circle through three points, by drawing the right bisectors of the joins of the points, it is only when these bisectors are in a pencil of the first kind, that we get a true circle. From the second kind we get a curve called the *"horocycle"*: it is the locus of images of a given point in a pencil of lines whose right rays (or left rays) are limit rays of each other; from the third kind we get the locus of the images of a given point in a set of lines all perpendicular to the same line, the axis; it is also

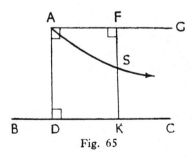

Fig. 65

the locus of a point at constant distance from that line, this locus is not straight, the interval joining any two of its points lies between the locus and the axis. (The "equidistant curve").

102. *Constructions.* To illustrate further we give two constructions:

(1) To draw a limit ray from A to BC (Bolyai).

Let D be the foot of the perpendicular from A to BC, let

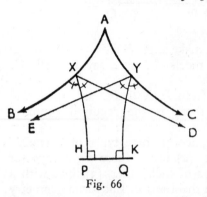

AG be perpendicular to DA, K a point on BC and F the foot of its perpendicular to AG; find S on FK so that $AS = DK$ (this requires the drawing of a circle). Then AS is the ray required.

(2) To draw a line whose rays are limit rays to two distinct rays (Hilbert).

Fig. 66

If AB, AC are the given rays, take points X, Y on them, equidistant from A.

Draw limit rays XD to AC, and YE to AB. Bisect the angles BXD, CYE by XH, YK. It can be proved that these do not cut, and are not limit rays of each other. Hence they have just one common perpendicular PQ. This is the line required.

If the given rays do not meet, then through any point A on one of them AB, draw a limit ray AC to the other line. The line whose rays are limit rays of AB, AC is that required.

If the given rays were themselves limit rays, we get lines which form an asymptotic triangle as in Fig. 67. This triangle has angle-sum zero, and its defect is the greatest possible, namely, two right angles. Accordingly its area exceeds that of any non-asymptotic triangle. This area is nevertheless *finite*.

103. *Hyperbolic trigonometry* is usually deduced by lengthy processes. To avoid these, we use intuitive methods, though

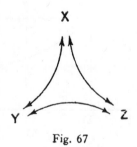

Fig. 67

these are risky, and we shall introduce forces and speak of their sums, or resultants. If the assumptions thus made do not lead to contradiction, there will be none when they are not made.

We assume that a force may be regarded as acting at any point along its line, that forces along the same line are added by adding their magnitudes, that forces at a point add to a force at that point (or cancel), and that the commutative and associative laws hold for the addition of forces.

If two forces of equal magnitudes P are inclined at an angle $2x$, denote the magnitude R of their resultant by $F(P, x)$, and suppose R acts along the bisector of the angle. If we add another pair of forces each of magnitude P' along the same lines, the magnitude of the resultant of this pair is $R'=F(P', x)$. The resultant of all four has magnitude $R+R'=F(P+P', x)$.

Hence $F(P, x) + F(P', x) = F(P + P', x)$,

which, if we assume that $F(P, x)$ is continuous in P, proves

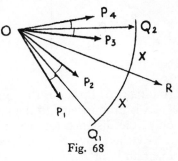

that $F(P, x)$ is proportional to P, and may be written as $2Pf(x)$. (The factor 2 is for convenience.)

Let P_1, P_2, P_3, P_4 be concurrent forces of equal magnitudes P, and let the angle between P_1, P_2, and also that between P_3, P_4, be $2y$. Let Q be the magnitude of the resultant Q_1 of P_1, P_2, and R the

Fig. 68

resultant of all four forces; and let Q_1, R be inclined at angle x.

Since R is the sum $(P_1 + P_2) + (P_3 + P_4)$, we have for its magnitude:
$$R = 2f(x).Q = 4f(x).f(y).P.$$
Since R is the sum $(P_1 + P_4) + (P_2 + P_3)$,
$$R = 2f(x + y).P + 2f(x - y).P.$$
Hence $\qquad f(x + y) + f(x - y) = 2f(x)f(y)$.

Of this functional equation, there are two types of continuous solutions. If $f(x) < 1$ for some value of x, the solution is $f(x) = \cos x/k$; but if $f(x) > 1$ for some value of x, then $f(x) = \operatorname{ch} x/k$ (k constant).

Thus if we assume that the magnitude of the resultant is not greater than the sum of the magnitudes of the components, we must take the first solution; if x is a right angle, the resultant of P and P inclined at angle $2x$ is zero.

Hence $k = 1$, $f(x) = \cos x$.

The resultant of two forces P inclined at angle $2x$ is $2P\cos x$, and from this it easily follows that the statics of forces *at a point* is the same as in Euclidean geometry.

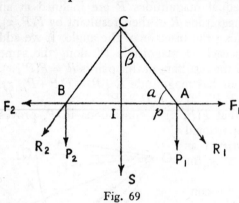

Fig. 69

Let equal forces P_1, P_2 act at A, B respectively, perpendicular to AB. Add equal and opposite forces F_1, F_2 along AB so that lines of action of the resultant R_1 of F_1 and P_1, and the resultant R_2 of F_2 and P_2 meet in C, say. Then R_1, R_2 have a resultant S through the mid-point I of AB.

S is proportional to the magnitude P of P_1, P_2 and depends on p, the distance IA; write $S = 2P\varphi(p)$.

By the above $S = 2R \cos \beta$, $P = R \sin \alpha$ where R is the magnitude of R_1, and $\alpha = \sphericalangle IAC$, $\beta = \sphericalangle ICA$.

Hence $S = 2P \cos \beta / \sin \alpha$, $\varphi(p) = \cos \beta / \sin \alpha$.

Since $\alpha + \beta < \pi/2$, we have $\varphi(p) > 1$.

Now take equal forces at A, A', B, B' where $IA = IB = a$, and $IA' = IB' = b$. Combine those at A, B, and then those at A', B' to find the resultant; then combine first those at A, A' and after that those at B, B'. Comparing, we have

$$\varphi(x + y) + \varphi(x - y) = 2\varphi(x)\varphi(y), \quad (a, b = x \pm y.)$$

Now since $\varphi(x) > 1$, we must take the solution

$$\varphi(x) = \operatorname{ch}(x/k)$$

Thence $\cos \beta / \sin \alpha = \operatorname{ch}(p/k)$, in triangle AIC of Fig. 69.

If we take p so that α is the angle of parallelism $\eta(p)$ for p,

then $\beta = 0$, $ch(p/k) =$ $1/\sin\eta(p)$, whence, since α is decreasing function of p, we deduce
$$\tan\tfrac{1}{2}\eta(p) = e^{-p/k}.$$

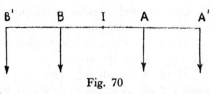

Fig. 70

These formulæ and the following were given by Lobatchefsky, and some by Bolyai. We have found a relation between a side of a right-angled triangle and its two acute angles. Drawing the altitude of the hypotenuse, we deduce the other relations, and then for any triangle by splitting it into right-angled triangles we can find:

$$\frac{sh(a/k)}{\sin A} = \frac{sh(b/k)}{\sin B} = \frac{sh(c/k),}{\sin C}$$

$$ch(c/k) = ch(a/k)ch(b/k) - sh(a/k)sh(b/k)\cos C.$$

104. From these formulæ all the hyperbolic trigonometry can be deduced. We notice the presence of a constant k of the nature of a length.

If k is large, the expansion of the first terms in the last formula gives

$$1 + \frac{c^2}{2k^2} = \left(1 + \frac{a^2}{2k^2}\right)\left(1 + \frac{b^2}{2k^2}\right) - \frac{ab}{k^2}\cos C,$$

or neglecting k^{-4}, $c^2 = a^2 + b^2 - 2ab\cos C$. For k large, the formula is close to the Euclidean. Hence for triangles *whose sides are small compared with k* we have approximately the Euclidean geometry. (Cf § 99 end.)

Readers familiar with spherical trigonometry will notice the close analogy between our formulæ and those in that theory. We obtain these if we replace sh, ch by sin, cos, and take k as the radius of the sphere.

105. *The question of consistency.* Having illustrated the difference between the present geometry and the Euclidean, we now discuss its self-consistency. We construct in Euclidean geometry a model of the hyperbolic geometry so that corresponding to any figure or theorem in the latter, there is one in the former. Contradictory theorems in the hyperbolic geometry,

if such existed, would correspond to contradictory theorems in the Euclidean geometry.

Hence *if* the Euclidean geometry is self-consistent, so is the hyperbolic geometry.

Here is the model. Take any circle C in the plane, fixed once for all. A circle orthogonal to C, or rather its arc inside C, shall correspond to a "line" of hyperbolic geometry; the points inside C shall correspond to "points" of hyperbolic geometry. (It will be convenient to use quotation marks for figures in hyperbolic geometry.)

Two circles orthogonal to C touching at a point of C correspond to "lines" containing "limit rays". It is a theorem

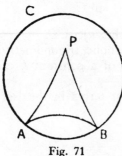

Fig. 71

of Euclidean geometry that, given a point P and a circle AB orthogonal to C at A, B, we can draw through P two circles orthogonal to C, one touching AB at A, the other doing so at B. This gives an analogue of our Axiom H: For any circle through P orthogonal to C, which goes inside angle APB, cuts AB inside C; the others through P do not.

Given two circles orthogonal to C, either (1) they meet in just one point inside C, or (2) they touch on C, or (3) they have a common orthogonal circle orthogonal to C. This corresponds to the three types of pairs of lines mentioned in § 100, provided that circles cutting orthogonally inside C (and cutting C orthogonally) correspond to "perpendicular lines". This can be secured, for the model may be developed so that the angle between two curves which meet inside C equals the "angle" between the "curves" they represent.

Distance is more complicated. If X, Y are points on a circle which cuts C orthogonally at P, Q, the "distance" between the corresponding "points" has to be taken as half the logarithm of the cross-ratio of P,X,Q,Y. A pencil of circles through X orthogonal to C, represents a "pencil of lines" through the "point" corresponding to X. A "rotation" round the "point" is represented by a transformation turning these circles into one another. The "path" of a "point" on a "rotating line" is represented by a circle coaxal with C with X as limiting point. Compare § 21.

A given "rotation" is the product of two "reflections" in two "lines", for the proof of this in §§ 2, 3 used congruence only. Corresponding to this in the model, the above transformation of the circles through X, leaving C invariant, is the product of inversions in two of them.

The group of hyperbolic "displacements" is represented by the group of transformations which turn circles into circles (or lines) and leave the circle C invariant.

106. *Projective geometry model* of hyperbolic geometry. Take any conic in the real projective plane and distinguish between inside and outside points. The points inside the conic and the intervals of lines inside the conic shall represent the "points" and "lines of hyperbolic geometry. The fact that "lines" are represented by lines is an advantage but it has to be paid for; in the previous model an "angle" was represented by an equal angle, but not here.

If the lines p, q cut the conic, and u, v be the tangents (real or not) to the conic from the point where p, q meet, the "angle" between the "lines" represented by p, q, is represented by the logarithm, divided by $2\sqrt{-1}$, of the cross ratio of p, u, q, v. It is real when p, q cut inside the conic.

This peculiar correspondence can be illustrated from Euclidean geometry. The conic is then replaced by the circular points I, J. Consider the lines $y = mx$, $y = ix$, $y = 0$, $y = -ix$; their cross-ratio is $(1 + im)/(1 - im)$ and its logarithm is $2i\theta$, where $\tan \theta = m$. And the line $y = mx$ *is* inclined at θ to the x-axis.

Returning to hyperbolic geometry, if P, Q be inside the conic and their join cuts the conic in U, V, the "distance" between the "points" represented by P, Q is represented by half the logarithm of the cross-ratio of P, U, Q, V.

Points on the conic then represent "points" at infinity; lines which meet on the conic correspond to "lines" which have "rays, limit rays of each other". Lines conjugate for the conic correspond to "perpendicular lines". The theorem of

the "common perpendicular" becomes: two lines, which cut
the conic, and meet outside it, have a common conjugate line
which cuts the conic. The conic is usually called the "*absolute
conic*" or the "*absolute*".

A "displacement" corresponds to a collineation which
leaves the conic invariant.

"Circles" correspond to conics which touch the absolute
at two distinct imaginary points; "equidistant curves" to
those which touch it at two distinct real points; we have
"horocycles" when the points of contact coincide.

107. *Spherical and Elliptic Geometry.* These two types of
classical non-Euclidean plane geometry are most quickly
grasped from their models in Euclidean space.

For spherical geometry, the "points" are represented by
points on a sphere, the "(straight) lines" by great circles;
"distances" between "points" by the lengths of the corresponding arcs, "angles" between "lines" by the angles between
corresponding great circles. The sum of the "angles" of a
"triangle" is now greater than two right angles and the excess
can be taken as a measure of the "area" of the "triangle".

For elliptic geometry, the model is similar, except that the
same "point" is represented by two antipodal points in the
sphere. In both geometries a "line" has a finite "length"; in
the first, any two "lines" meet in two "points", in the second,
in just one. There are no parallel lines.

Both geometries can of course be set up abstractly,
without a model. Elliptic geometry is merely projective
geometry endowed with a metric.

We can also construct a model in which "lines" are represented by circles in a plane, which cut a given circle diametrically (§ 25). The relation of this to the model on a sphere is
seen if we project the sphere stereographically from the North
pole on to the plane of the equator.

108. *Space.* All three geometries can be extended to three
dimensions. This leads to an interesting surface in the case of
elliptic and spherical geometry which can be easily visualized.
Whereas in the Euclidean geometry there are lines (parallels)
with an infinite number of common perpendiculars, but not

in the hyperbolic geometry, in the elliptic and spherical geometries, we can have two *skew* lines with an infinite number of common perpendiculars.

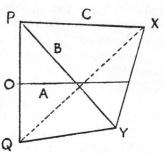

Fig. 72

Namely, if *OP* is perpendicular to *OA*, there are two lines *PB*, *PC* through *P* each of which has an infinite number of perpendiculars, common with *OA*. These are the "*Clifford parallels*" (1873). From *Q*, the image of *P* in *OA*, go two other Clifford parallels, and they meet those from *P*, in *X*, *Y* say. *XY* is perpendicular to *OA* and to the four parallels. In spherical space, *PX*, *QX* meet again in a point *X'*, and *PY*, *QY* again in *Y'*, where *X'Y'* is the image of *XY* in *PQ*. But in elliptic space there is no counter-line *X'Y'*,

If now we rotate the whole figure round the line *OA*, then our lines *PX*, *PY*, *QX*, *QY* describe a surface like an anchor ring in general shape, the "*Clifford surface*."

The surprising fact about this surface is that *on it* we have a kind of Euclidean geometry; in any region of the surface the theorem of Pythagoras holds for the shortest curves which can be drawn on the surface. Dwellers in elliptic space who wished for a model of a Euclidean plane would point to this Clifford surface. But no model is perfect; our models of the infinite hyperbolic plane were finite regions of the Euclidean plane; and this model of the Euclidean plane has a *finite* area in elliptic space. It is thus more correct to say it represents a finite piece of the Euclidean plane.

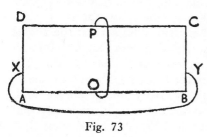

Fig. 73

Take a rectangle in the Euclidean plane and identify corresponding points of opposite sides, regarding *X*, *Y* as the same point, and *P*, *Q* as the same point. With a little persuasion of the material we could in fact make these points coincide. Our Clifford surface corresponds to the rectangle with these identifications.

In hyperbolic space there is a surface analogous to the horocycle in a plane. On this surface, too, the geometry is Euclidean.

We can construct a model of hyperbolic space by taking points inside a quadric, the "absolute" quadric. (Chap. VII.)

109. *Geometry and Experience.* The reader has probably asked, which of these possible geometries is true? We will try to explain why this question, so expressed, is wrongly put.

Geometry, as we shall see later, can be developed as a purely abstract doctrine, not connected with the external world. To get an interpretation in experience, we must match the abstract ideas with something concrete, we must decide, for example, what we regard as a straight line. We might suggest a ray of light, a tightly-stretched string, an axis of rotation. But all these things are physical things, and we cannot test the geometry without assuming the physical laws they are supposed to obey, nor can we test these laws without assuming some geometry.

Again if we regard interstellar space as empty (a physical assumption), and postulate that rays of light in vacuo are straight (another physical assumption), we may ascertain by some means (finally by some astronomical definition), the distances from us of two remote nebulæ. Unfortunately we cannot ourselves measure their cross-country distance apart; suppose someone else does this, using our methods. At the same time, let the angles of the triangle formed by the earth and the two nebulæ be measured. We now have three sides and three angles of a triangle, and can test whether they satisfy the relations of Euclidean geometry or not.

Some difficulties, however, remain. The sum of the angles of a Euclidean triangle is *exactly* two right angles, but all measurement is *approximate*. A dogmatic assertion that the Euclidean formulæ hold, can never be proved. Suppose, however, we found that the formulæ of hyperbolic geometry hold, with a value of k, found approximately. Ought we to say that the geometry of space is hyperbolic? We should be compelled to do so if we still assumed that the rays of light were straight, but there is no compulsion to assume this, and if we assumed instead that they were appropriately curved, we could re-introduce Euclidean geometry. But we might wish to postulate a physical cause for this curvature, and then, once again, we have to test a combination of physics and geometry.

There is another way out: we could restore the Euclidean geometry and keep straight rays, if we adjusted the lengths of the sides of the triangle; we can do this by assuming that the velocity of light is not the same along all three sides. This is again a physical assumption, and it brings in an extra con-sideration, the measurement of time.

Summing up: we ought not to ask which geometry is *true*. We can only enquire whether a particular complete theory combining geometry, physics, and time-measurements is verified by experience and suitable matchings. If this is so, then within the combination, one of the three components can be varied, if the others are suitably modified.

We ought to seek the simplest combination of the three components. Let us hope that observations with the new 200 inch reflector will be of service here.

109*a*. If we anticipate Chap. VII, we can say a little more about the projective model of hyperbolic geometry mentioned on p. 94. Take any quadric as absolute. (Think of an ellipsoid.) Use quotation marks as on p. 90. The "points" of hyperbolic space are represented by points inside the ellipsoid, the "lines" and "planes" by the parts of lines and planes inside the ellip-soid. A "line" contains a "ray", which is a "limit ray" for a "plane", when the corresponding line and plane meet on the absolute. Thus the "limit rays" to a "plane" which go through a "point" do not lie in a "plane". Two intersecting "lines" are "perpendicular" when each meets the polar line of the other for the absolute.

CHAPTER VI

THE LOGICAL STRUCTURE OF GEOMETRIES

110. WE now consider in some detail, the logical structure of various geometries. The treatment will be abstract, and we advise the reader to glance again at sections 62–64 where the abstract view is explained.

We ought of course to begin at the beginning, but consideration for the reader prompts us to begin with congruence, which is some distance on in the development, and if anyone reading the first few sections feels that further analysis is still needed, he may be assured that this is only postponed.

111. *The theory of congruence* is usually based on the notion of the congruence of triangles and this on the notions of the equality or congruence, of intervals and angles. We first reduce the two latter notions to one.

Two triangles are said to be *"congruent"* when the sides of one are congruent* to corresponding sides of the other, and the angles to the angles. A side is an interval, and we achieve a simplification if we think of its ends only, that is, of a point-pair.

We take as the fundamental *undefined* notion, the congruence of point-pairs, as in the phrase, "the pair (A, B) is congruent to (C, D)". The pairs are *ordered* pairs of distinct points; that is, if we speak of a pair (A, B) it is understood that A, B are distinct, and (A, B) is distinguished from (B, A). The reader may *interpret* the phrase above by thinking that a pair of dividers with ends at A, B can be transferred to have its ends at C, D.

We shall reduce the notions of the congruence of intervals and of angles to this notion. But, first, we can define the congruence relation for any figures, where by a *"figure"* we mean any set of points, either separated, or arranged in curves, surfaces, or solids.

---

* For intervals and angles the usual word here is unfortunately "equal".

If two figures F_1, F_2 can be put into *one-to-one correspondence* (p. 57) in such a way that when points P_1, Q_1 in F_1 correspond to P_2, Q_2, in F_2, then always the point-pair (P_1, Q_1) is congruent to (P_2, Q_2), we say that F_1, F_2 are "*congruent*". (If they happen to be plane figures, we can picture this by thinking that F_1 can be moved to coincide with F_2, so that each point of F_1 coincides with the corresponding point of F_2.)

Now an angle is a figure, if by an "*angle*" we mean, as we shall, just two rays (or half-lines) with a common origin. Two angles AOB, CPD are thus defined to be congruent when each point on one of the rays OA, OB can be matched with just one on one of the rays PC or PD, all points of both angles being thus used, and if, when X, Y are on OA or OB, and X', Y' their mates, then (X, Y) is congruent to (X', Y'). We do not demand that O corresponds to P.

In the same way the congruence of intervals is reduced to that of point-pairs by matching the points of one interval with those of the other; we do not demand that end-points correspond to end-points.

112. *The axioms of congruence.* As we take the congruence of point-pairs as an undefined relation we must assume nothing about it, except what is stated in the axioms; we must take care that we do not draw from the interpretations mentioned above, any extra properties.

Ax. 1. If (A, B) is a point-pair, and $A'X$ any ray from A', then there is just one point B' on this ray such that (A, B) is congruent to (A', B').

Ax. 2. If (A, B) is congruent to (C, D), and (C, D) to (E, F), then (A, B) is congruent to (E, F).

Ax. 3. If A, B, C are on a line, and B is between A and C, and if A', B', C' are on a line, and B' is between A' and C', and if (A, B) and (B, C) be respectively congruent to (A', B') and (B', C'), then (A, C) is congruent to (A', C').

Ax. 4. (A, B) is congruent to (B, A).

From these, with the strictest logical rigour, we can prove that if (A, B) is congruent to (C, D), then so is (C, D) to (A, B), and further, that (A, B) is congruent to itself. These were *not* stated in the axioms. We can also shew that if two intervals

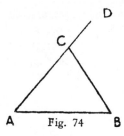

Fig. 74

are congruent, then end-points must correspond to end-points. In view of this and Axs. 3, 4 we may say "*AB* is congruent to *CD*" instead of "(*A*, *B*) is congruent to (*C*, *D*)".

All questions on the congruence of intervals, rays, and lines can now be answered. To investigate plane figures we need only one more axiom:

Ax. 5. If *A*, *B*, *C* are non-collinear points, and *A*, *C*, *D* are collinear, with *C* between *A* and *D*, and if analogous relations hold between *A'*, *B'*, *C'*, *D'*, and if *AB*, *BC*, *CA*, *AD* are respectively congruent to *A'B'*, *B'C'*, *C'A'*, *A'D'*, then *BD* is congruent to *B'D'*.

113. *Consequences of these Axioms*. We state some deductions, roughly in the order in which they may be obtained. At the risk of being tedious, we say again that nothing about congruence may be used, except what is deduced from the axioms. In particular, there is no provision for superposition, the use of circles, or parallels, or continuity arguments.

It is first easy to remove the restriction on *D* in Ax. 5 and to prove the modification when *D* is any point on the line *AC*.

Then three non-collinear points cannot be congruent to three collinear points. We sketch the proof of this to give the reader an idea of the type of argument. The theorem can be reduced to the case: three non-collinear points (*A*, *B*, *C*) cannot be congruent to (*A*, *B'*, *C*), where *B'* is on the interval *AC*.

We do not yet know whether an interval *BB'* has a midpoint, but we can prove from Axs. 1–4 that it has not more than one. Take *N* on *BB'* not at its mid-point, if it has one, and *L* on *BB'* with *BN* congruent to *B'L*; hence *L*, *N* are distinct. Then from Ax. 5, it follows that *AN* is congruent to *AL*, and *CN* to *CL*, and thence *B'N* is congruent to *B'L*, contrary to Ax. 1.

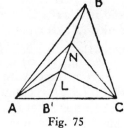

Fig. 75

By similar arguments, often very hard to discover, we can shew that, for two congruent triangles, vertices correspond to vertices; the definition of congruent triangles is, with us, a special case of the definition we gave of congruent figures; we can shew that angles adjacent to congruent angles are congruent, and that vertically opposite angles are congruent. We cannot use the classical proof of the last, for we know nothing yet about the sum of two angles, nor about right angles, not even whether they exist.

Next it follows that we cannot have two distinct congruent angles BAC, BAD with the same arm AB and with C, D on the same side of the arm. The theorems on the congruence of triangles which concern three sides, two sides and the included angle, and two angles and the side between them, now follow. That congruence which concerns two angles and a side *not* between, can only be shewn after it has been proved that if Q, P, A are collinear and D, B on the same side of QA and angles QPD, QAB be congruent, then the lines PD, AB cannot meet. The proof of this on p. 83 can be transferred here. It breaks down for spherical and elliptic geometries. Cf. § 118.

Defining a right angle as one congruent to an adjacent angle, it can be shewn such angles exist, that they are all congruent, that perpendiculars can be drawn from any point to any line, that every interval has a mid-point, and that an angle with a given arm can be constructed congruent to a given angle. It is the last theorem which gives point to the whole structure. Before it is established, we do not know how wide is the class of congruent angles.

The only basic construction to be used is that derived from Ax. 1.

The addition and subtraction of intervals and angles can be defined and the fundamental properties proved; in particular the sum of two sides of a triangle is greater than the third side.

It can be shewn that parallel lines exist, but the Euclidean parallel axiom cannot be proved, and all the above is valid in hyperbolic geometry. No additional congruence axiom is needed for three dimensions; in particular, it can be shewn that all right angles in space are congruent.

The results of this section are due to a long chain of workers beginning with the Greeks. The discovery that only Axs. 1–5 are needed is due to J. L. Dorroh.

The author has recently noticed that it is sufficient to assume a form of Ax. 5 in the two cases when the pair A', B' coincides with A, B or with B, A. This is a further simplification.

114. *Circles*. There are still some questions left. Given a triangle ABC and a ray $A'X$, we can find a point B' on $A'X$, and a point C' on a given side of $A'X$ such that ABC is congruent to $A'B'C'$. A given triangle can be reproduced anywhere.

But if we are given three intervals (the sum of the lengths of any two exceeding that of the third), we cannot yet shew that there is a triangle whose sides have the lengths of these intervals. For this we need:

The Circle Axiom. A circle which goes through a point inside and a point outside a given circle, meets it.

This was *tacitly* assumed by Euclid in his first proof. Actually we need assume the axiom only in the case when the points mentioned are on a line through the centre of the given circle; we can then shew that, in the general case, the circles cut in just two points, and further that a line which goes through a point inside the circle meets it in just two points.

115. *Axioms of Order*. We must now dig deeper. In spite of what we said about not reading results from figures, we did so in the previous sections, for we assumed that only one line joined two points, we spoke of rays or half-lines, of opposite sides of lines, and of points inside circles. Such relations were the last to be analysed, and until the 'nineties all geometric proofs (at any rate, of ordinary geometry), involved essential appeal to figures; thus if a line in a plane cut a side of a triangle in the plane, it was tacitly assumed that it cut another side or passed through the opposite vertex, and this was read from the figure.

It is our ambition to read *nothing* from the figure, but to proceed abstractly. As a recompense for these labours, we gain an understanding of the fundamental essential properties of geometry, not possessed by earlier workers.

We take as our basis a three-termed relation, and make specific assumptions on it. Consider the relation "*A* prefers *C* to *B*". With the usual meaning of these words; it is then false that *A* prefers *B* to *C*, and human relations might be so nicely adjusted, that it always followed as a consequence that *C* preferred *A* to *B*.

Let us write (*ABC*) for the proposition "*A* prefers *C* to *B*". We then have:

(*ABC*) implies that (*ACB*) is false and that (*CBA*) is true. The three-termed relation we shall take has these properties as well as some others.

We take then as undefined, a class of elements called "points" (the things we are talking about), and a three-termed relation which holds between some ordered triads of points, but not between all triads and which for any given ordered triad, is either true, or false.

The three-termed relation between *A*, *B*, *C*, or rather the assertion that it holds, will be written (*ABC*). This is then the symbol of a proposition true or false.

Now assume

Ax. 1. If (*ABC*) is true, then *A*, *B*, *C* are distinct.

Ax. 2. If (*ABC*) is true, then (*BCA*) is false.

(The reader might consider such interpretations for (*ABC*) as: *AB* is perpendicular to *BC*; *A*, *C* are on a circle, centre *B*; *B* is the mid-point of *AC*, and test which Axioms are valid. An intuitive interpretation which will fit them all is: *B* is on the line *AC* and between *A* and *C*.)

If *A*, *B* are distinct points, the set of points *P* such that either (*PAB*) or (*APB*) or (*ABP*) is true, is called the "*line*" *AB*.

Ax. 3. If *C*, *D* be distinct points of the line *AB*, then *A*, *B* are (distinct) points of the line *CD*.

From these three axioms we can prove that, if (*ABC*) is true, then so is (*CBA*), but that (*BCA*), (*CAB*), (*ACB*), (*BAC*) are all false; and that, if *A*, *B* be distinct points, there is just one line on which both lie.

If our abstract relation is to have all the properties which we should ascribe to one-dimensional order in the intuitive interpretation we mentioned, we must have besides Axs. 1, 2, the following from which all the desired properties can, in fact, be deduced:

The Axioms of one dimensional order are Axs. 1, 2 and

  (a) (ABC) implies (CBA).
  (b) If A, B, C be distinct then at least one of (ABC), (BCA), (CAB), (CBA), (ACB), (BAC) is true.
  (c) If A, B, C, X are distinct, then (ABC) implies (ABX) or (XBC).

We can then shew

  (d) (XAB), (ABY) together imply (XAY).
  (e) (XAB), (AYB) together imply (XAY).

Now of these (a) can be shewn, as we said from Axs. 1, 2, 3, while (b) follows from the definition of a line, if A, B, C are on a line. As to (c), (d), (e) they can be shewn from the axioms we will give. But first let us make sure we have enough points.

Ax. 4. (*External convexity.*) If A, B be distinct points, there is at least one point C such that (ABC) is true.

Ax. 5. (*Two dimensions.*) There are three points not on the same line.

Now comes what may be regarded as the central axiom:

Ax. 6. (*Veblen.*) If A, B, C are distinct and A not on the line BC, and if (BCD), (CEA) be true, then there is a point F on the line DE such that (AFB) is true.

From Axs. 1 – 6 follow (c), (d), (e) and all theorems on the order of points on a line which are intuitively true in our interpretation; also we get the convexity theorem: if A, B be distinct points there is a point X such that (AXB) is true, and using (d) (e), there is an infinite number of such points. Also in Ax. 6 we can shew that (DEF) holds.

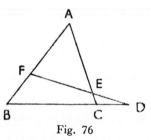

Fig. 76

116. *The Plane.* By Ax. 5, there are three non-collinear points A, B, C. We might define the plane ABC as: (1) the set of all points on the lines which join pairs of points on the sides of the triangle, or as: (2) the set of

all points on the lines which join the vertices to points of the opposite sides (including the vertices in the sides).

Each of these definitions follows from the other in the presence of our axioms, though it would give the reader great pains to prove this. Also from either it can be shewn: that if X, Y, Z be non-collinear points on the plane ABC, then A, B, C are on the plane XYZ, and every point on one of the planes ABC, XYZ is on the other.

All the theorems on order in a plane usually assumed from geometric intuition can now be proved, such as those which relate to the two sides of a line in a plane, or those which concern the inside and outside of polygons, or the splitting up of the inside of a polygon into triangles. For instance, we can define a *simple* polygon as, roughly, one which does not cut itself, and then shew that points of the plane not on the polygon are of two kinds, that two points of the same kind can be joined by a zig-zag line (which can easily be defined), which does not meet the polygon, while those of different kinds cannot be so joined, and further there are points of one of the two kinds, but not of the other, which lie on a line not meeting the polygon. This done, we can speak of the *exterior* and *interior* of the polygon.

117. *Space*, To get three dimensions we need only assume:
Ax. 7. Not all points are in the same plane.

If then A, B, C, D are non coplanar points, we can define the *"space $ABCD$"* in either of the two ways analogous to our definitions of the plane above, and prove their equivalence.

To restrict ourselves to three dimensions we may assume:
Ax. 8. All points are in the same space.

Axioms 1 – 8 are called *"order axioms"*, and a geometry which satisfies them, will be called a *"descriptive geometry"* of three dimensions.

The axioms of congruence have now been underpinned, and these with the axioms of order serve as a basis (incomplete) either of Euclidean or of the hyperbolic geometry, or generally, of a *"congruence geometry"*.

118. *Non-cutting lines*. From the axioms of order we can deduce that two lines cannot cut in two points, but we cannot

decide whether all pairs in a plane cut, or whether there are some that do not. We proved, however, from the congruence theorems on p. 83 that non-cutting lines exist in the plane. If we re-examine this proof we see that it assumes: (1) two lines cannot meet in two points, (2) a line divides a plane in which it lies into two sides (otherwise in Fig. 61 it might happen that the "two" points in which PE and AE cut coincided).

Now although both of these assumptions follow from our axioms of order, yet (1) fails in spherical geometry, and (2) fails in elliptic geometry, for in that geometry a line does not divide a plane in which it lies into two sides; we can draw another straight line from one side of the given line to the other side without meeting the line. Our order axioms do not all hold for these geometries, although they all hold for hyperbolic geometry.

119. *Relation to projective geometry.* When we wish to compare Euclidean and projective geometry, we introduce points at infinity in the former, and say that a set of parallel lines goes through such a point. We can, however, avoid the creation of these extra points by turning slightly the discussion. Define a *"bundle"* as the set of lines and planes through a given point, *or* a set of parallel lines and the planes through them. Make this bundle correspond to a point; in the first case to the point in which the lines and planes meet, and in the second to the "point at infinity" in which they meet in the earlier formulation. Statements on points, whether at infinity or not, can then be translated into statements on these bundles.

If we do not assume the Euclidean parallel axiom, the matter becomes more complicated; for example, in hyperbolic geometry we have several types of bundles. (Cf. § 100.)

Our descriptive geometry is more general than the hyperbolic, but the notion of the bundle still works. Take two coplanar lines l, m, then take all lines n in which any plane through l meets any through m, and then take all lines r in which any plane through any of the lines n cuts the plane lm. If the lines l, m cut, all the lines constructed go through the point of cutting. In any case, each pair of the constructed lines can be shewn to be coplanar, and this set of lines and the planes through the pairs will be called a *"bundle"*. Given any two bundles, there is a set of planes common to them, this set is called the *"pencil contained* in the two bundles".

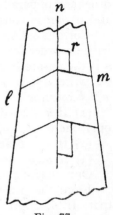

Fig. 77

If now in our axioms of three dimensional projective geometry, we replace "point" by "bundle", and "line through two points" by "pencil contained in two bundles", we can prove from our order axioms that the projective axioms of § 93 hold. The investigation is by no means easy, but it shews that *we can make our descriptive geometry projective.*

We need three dimensions to do this; it cannot be done in two only, for a descriptive form of Desargues' theorem has to be deduced. After it has been done, it is more suggestive to speak of points, lines, and planes "at infinity", and to look on these phrases as a translation of phrases which speak of bundles and pencils.

Our space being three dimensional, Desargues' theorem holds (§ 93), but it must be suitably formulated, since some of the figure may be at infinity. Using the results of Chap. IV, we have the amazing conclusion:

In any descriptive geometry of three or more dimensions, we can introduce co-ordinates, and erect a co-ordinate geometry, our co-ordinates being elements of a quasi-field. We can create magnitudes from a mere muchness.

120. *Ordered projective geometry.* To bring our descriptive and projective geometries into closer correspondence, we introduce order into the latter. We select any plane for the "plane at infinity"; the points of this are not to be in a relation of order to any other points. On these other points we impose a relation, satisfying our order axioms, and such that the lines and planes defined by means of it, are the lines and planes of the projective geometry. If we call lines "parallel" when they meet on the plane at infinity, the properties of

order and of parallels will be the same as in Euclidean geometry, and if *that* is consistent, we need fear no contradiction here.

Corresponding to the order imposed on our points, we shall have an order in our co-ordinate quasi-field, namely (p. 74), if a is the co-ordinate of A on OU and (AOU) or (OUA) holds, we write $a < 0$, and if (OAU) holds, we write $a > 0$. Let $a > b$ mean $a - b > 0$. It can then be proved:

(1) If a, b be distinct elements of the quasi-field, one and only one of $a > b$, $a < b$, holds.

(2) If $a < b$ and $b < c$, then $a < c$.

(3) If a, $b > 0$ then $a + b > 0$, $ab > 0$.

Our quasi-field is then an *ordered quasi-field*.

From the projective and order axioms it easily follows that: If A, B are harmonic conjugates with respect to C, D, then one of A, B is between C and D, and the other is not.

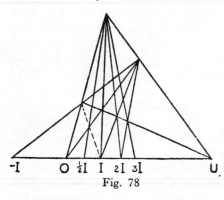

Fig. 78

Whether we have an ordered projective geometry, or a descriptive geometry which has been made projective, we can construct a *"rational net"* on a line; that is, starting from points O, I, U on a line, where (OIU) holds we can construct $I + I$, $I + I + I, \ldots$ which call $2I, 3I, \ldots,$ and also, with an obvious notation, $\frac{1}{2}I, \frac{1}{3}I, \frac{2}{3}I, \ldots,$ and their negatives; in fact, each rI where r is a positive or negative rational number.

We can do this even though our co-ordinates, as a whole, form a quasi-field only; the elements of form rI (r rational), form of course, a *field* in this quasi-field.

121. *Pappus' theorem.* If we wish our co-ordinates to form a field (Cf. § 88) it is enough if we assume either (1) or (2):

(1) Between any two points of our line there is an element of our rational net.

(2) If a, b be given positive elements of our quasi-field,

there is a natural number n such that $a + a + \ldots + a$ to n terms exceeds b. (Cf. Archimedes' Axiom, p. 109.)

Thus in an ordered projective geometry, either of these assumptions (they are in fact equivalent), will give us Pappus' theorem. Finite projective geometries and geometries with complex co-ordinates are ruled out here, since their corresponding fields cannot be ordered in our way.

122. Pappus' theorem can also be proved in congruence geometry, even in two dimensions, but all the known proofs are very complicated. If, however, we adjoin the Euclidean parallel axiom, we have a great simplification; we can deduce the properties of cyclic quadrilaterals and thence the affine case of Pappus' theorem (§ 88). From this, not so easily, follows Desargues' theorem (even if we use two dimensions only, Cf. § 93), and the complete Pappus' theorem. In the next section we need only the affine forms of these.

We can now consider Euclidean geometry.

123. *Similar figures* are a distinctive feature of Euclidean geometry; they do not exist in the non-Euclidean. The difficulties which the Greeks encountered in their study centred round the fact that two intervals can be incommensurable, the ratio of their lengths being, as we should say, irrational. It is easy for us to avoid these difficulties.

The method by which we introduced co-ordinates in projective geometry can be applied, with simplifications, to the Euclidean. Now that we have congruence, our Fig. 54 in which we defined $C = A + B$ leads to $OC = OA + OB$, where $OA, \ldots$ are lengths of intervals, and the sum of lengths is defined in the obvious way. Lines meeting on l are now replaced by parallel lines.

Again, if O, A, F are in line, and O, X, Y in line, and AX parallel to FY (Fig. 79), let us say $OA/OF = OX/OY$. Then if O, X', Y' are in line, and OX', OY' congruent to OX, OY,

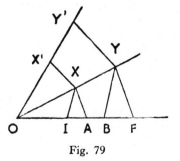

Fig. 79

we have by the *affine** case of Desargues' theorem, that AX' is parallel to FY', and so $OA/OF = OX'/OY'$; thus we may regard the relation as holding between the *lengths* of intervals, and this justifies the notation.

If now we adapt the definition of multiplication in § 87 to the situation here, we see that *for lengths of intervals*, $a/b = c/d$ and $ad = bc$ are equivalent statements.

Pappus' theorem in its affine form (§ 88), gives us again $ab = ba$.

The usual theorems on similar triangles now follow, and also Pythagoras' theorem, not indeed as a theorem on areas, but as one of type $a^2 + b^2 = c^2$.

We again point out that the lengths a, b, ... are not necessarily ordinary real numbers; continuity has *not* been assumed.

124. *Areas and Euclidean geometry*. As we can define the product of lengths, and construct a theory of similar triangles on the basis of the axioms of order, congruence and parallels, we may define the area of a triangle as half the product of the length of a side and the corresponding height, and prove that it is independent of the side chosen.

We can define the area of a polygon as the sum of the areas of the triangles into which it can be split, and prove that it is independent of the manner of splitting, for the "intuitive" theorems we need about the splitting up of polygons can be deduced from our order axioms.

It is *not* necessary to assume, as was long thought, that it is impossible to split up a polygon into triangles and then to fit them together to cover a portion of the polygon only, for this impossibility can be proved. Euclid made this assumption, stating it rather oracularly as "the whole is greater than the part".

It is rather surprising that if we have two polygons of equal areas it does not follow, *as a general theorem*, from our axioms of order, congruence and parallels, that they are "*equivalent by addition*", i.e. that we can split one up into triangles and fit these together to make the other. To prove this can *always* be done, we must assume *Archimedes' Axiom:*

---

* Corresponding sides of the triangles parallel.

Given two lengths, a multiple of the smaller can be found which exceeds the larger.*

To shew it in *special instances*, the extra Axiom is not needed.

If, however, we also call two polygons "*equivalent*" when they can be obtained by subtracting polygons, equivalent by addition, from two polygons equivalent by addition (which does not imply they are themselves equivalent by addition), then we can shew, without the Axiom of Archimedes, that polygons with equal areas are equivalent in this sense.

In shewing that parallelograms on the same base and of the same height were equivalent, Euclid had to use subtraction.

125. *Volumes* in Euclidean geometry present unexpected difficulties. We can define the volume of a tetrahedron as one-third of the area of a face multiplied by the corresponding height, and prove that this is independent of the face chosen, and define the volume of a polyhedron as the sum of the volumes of the tetrahedra into which it can be split, and prove that this is independent of the method of splitting; the "intuitive" theorems on splitting which are needed can be deduced from the axioms of order.

But, and this makes a great difference between the theory of volumes and areas; we cannot, for example, split up a regular tetrahedron into tetrahedra and fit them together to make a cube. Polyhedra with equal volumes need not be equivalent, either by addition or in the extended sense when subtraction is permitted, even if we assume the Axiom of Archimedes.

Some new method or assumption is needed. Euclid split his solids up into "infinitely thin" slices; this brings in continuity.

It is interesting that similar difficulties arise for "hyper-volumes" in Euclidean space of any odd number of dimensions, but not for an *even* number of dimensions.

126. *Constructions* are really existence theorems; they tell us that, from the existence of certain elements, we can, from our axioms deduce the existence of others.

Suppose that in congruence geometry, besides assuming that we can draw the line joining two points, and find the cut, if it exists, of two lines, we assume only this:

* You will always reach home, if you walk long enough.

An interval congruent to a *fixed* interval, the *"gauge"*, can be cut off from any point on any ray.

Constructions carried out with these means are called *gauge constructions*.

We can then perform many constructions usually done by ruler and compasses: we can bisect intervals and angles, draw the perpendicular from any point to any line, and cut off from any point on any ray an interval congruent to *any* given interval.

If now we adjoin the Euclidean parallel axiom, not yet used, we can draw the parallel to a given line through a given point, and we can also cut down our gauge assumption to the following, and still perform the above constructions:

There is a fixed point O such that the gauge can be cut off from O on any ray from O; that is, we have a "gauge circle", centre O, and know its cuts with any line through its centre.

To get all ruler and compass constructions, in Euclidean geometry, we need assume only that we know the cuts of the gauge-circle and *any* line which cuts it.

In connection with this, we noted that to complete the theory of congruence, we adjoined the circle-axiom (§ 114). If we have the Euclidean parallel axiom it is sufficient to assume, instead of this, that a line through the inside of a certain fixed circle, and in its plane, meets it.

To go deeper, we use co-ordinates. By ruler constructions only, assuming we can draw parallels, we can construct, in Euclidean geometry, the points on the x-axis whose distances from the origin are $a + b$, $a - b$, ab and a/b, if we have those whose distances are a, b. If we adjoin the gauge construction and use Pythagoras, we can also construct the point whose distance from the origin is $(a^2 + b^2)^{\frac{1}{2}}$. But, even if $a > b$, we can*not* so construct the point at distance $(a^2 - b^2)^{\frac{1}{2}}$, for this we need the extra construction above on the gauge circle.

The algebraical counterpart of a construction involving lines and circles, will be a problem of solving certain linear and quadratic equations, and a point whose construction is required will have co-ordinates which can be obtained from those of the given points by a series of rational operations and the extraction of square roots. If the least number of square roots which must be used is n, there will be 2^n solutions if all the square roots are roots of positive quantities. For some problems this will be the case for *all* positions of the given points; the problem can then be solved by gauge constructions. For others the square roots may be roots of negative quantities for some positions of the given points, and there will then be fewer than 2^n solutions; such problems cannot be solved by gauge constructions, they need the full compass constructions. A simple example is the construction: to draw a circle through two points to touch a given line. If the points are on opposite sides of the line, there is no solution.

The proof of these statements depends on a deep theorem of algebra: If $f(p_1 \ldots, p_n)$ is a rational function with rational coefficients, which is never negative when $p_1, \ldots, p_n$ are real, then it can be expressed as the sum of squares of rational functions of $p_1, \ldots, p_n$ with rational coefficients. (Hilbert.)

(A rational function is a polynomial divided by a polynomial.)

A regular polygon which can be constructed by ruler and compasses can be constructed by gauge constructions. Which polygons are these? As it is obvious, that if one of n sides can be so constructed, then so can one of $2n$ sides, we need only consider the case when n is odd. We get these possible n as follows: write down all *primes* which are one more than a power of 2, viz, 3, 5, 17, 257, 65537 (no one knows if there are any more). Then n is either one of these or a product of *distinct* numbers of the set. Thus a regular 17-gon or 51-gon, but not a regular 9-gon can be constructed by gauge constructions, or ruler and compass constructions.

The proof of this again depends on a deep theorem in the theory of numbers. (Gauss.)

127. *Continuity*. The simplest way to introduce continuity would be to assume that our co-ordinates were numbers of the real continuum, but it is better to join up this assumption with the order axioms.

The essence of the continuity assumption is easily explained. If the interval of time from A.D. 1600–1700 was a mathematical continuum then (assuming the royalist theory), *either* there was a last instant in the reign of Charles I and no first instant in the reign of Charles II, *or* there was no last instant of the first reign, but there was a first instant of the second reign. When the indictment of the regicides was under consideration, the lawyers could not decide in whose reign the decapitation took place.

Formally, if the points of an interval be divided into two sets, with no common point, but each containing at least two points, and if no point of one set is ever between two of the other, then there is just one point which is between any two points (distinct from itself), of different sets: (we can shew it is not between two points of the same set).

If this holds we say the interval is a "*continuum*".

It is enough if we assume this for just one interval. Its influence is far reaching.

(1) If we have three dimensions we can now deduce from the order axioms that a plane contains non-cutting lines (we can even deduce *this* in two dimensions only).

(2) If, for each line in each plane, there is a point in the plane (the point may vary with the line), for which the Euclidean parallel axiom holds, it holds generally.

(3) Otherwise the hyperbolic axiom holds in the form given in Chap. V.

(4) We can construct a Euclidean geometry in the descriptive three-dimensional geometry, if we assume the parallel axiom in the form given in (2). For then we can deduce the projective axioms with a plane at infinity, and using Desargues' theorem, which follows since we have three dimensions, we can introduce co-ordinates which form a quasi-field. The continuity axiom leads to a similar continuity property in these co-ordinates, from this Archimedes' Axiom (§ 121) follows, and hence the quasi-field is a field. In this we can build up a co-ordinate Euclidean geometry, by defining distance (§ 91) and hence congruence, for positive quantities now have square roots (by continuity), a fact which also gives the circle axiom.

128. *The angle sum of a triangle.* In a congruence geometry in two dimensions, we can shew that, if the angle sum in *one*

triangle is respectively greater than, equal to, or less than two right angles, it is so in all, and that if the Axiom of Archimedes on lengths be assumed, the first case is impossible. But if we do not assume that Axiom we could have an infinite number of lines through a point not cutting a given coplanar line, and yet have the angle sum greater than, or equal to, two right angles. Ax. H of Chap. IV would not of course hold; there would not be any limit rays.

129. *Consistency of Euclidean Geometry.* In shewing that the non-Euclidean Geometries were consistent, we assumed the consistency of Euclidean geometry. The latter question can obviously be reduced to the question of the consistency of the co-ordinate geometry. If we do not assume continuity, the question is then that of the consistency of the axioms for a field, and if we assume continuity, the question concerns the axioms for a continuum.

The genetic theory of algebra begins with axioms for integers, and definitions by induction of addition and multiplication of integers. From these it is easy to construct a system satisfying the axioms of a field. Thus the question is reduced to that of the consistency of the theory of integers, the consistency of arithmetic. It is not unreasonable to assume consistency here, although as is well known, Gödel has shewn that the consistency cannot be *proved* inside the scheme itself.

The question of the consistency of the axioms of the continuum is much harder; this has never been proved in any way, and is even doubted by some. We have seen that the continuum assumption can be postponed if we wish, but other treatments of geometry place it in the fore-front.

130. *The Erlanger Programme of Klein.* We have classified geometries by means of their axioms. There is another way which we will illustrate: projective geometry deals with the properties of figures which are not changed by collineations; inversion geometry with those not changed by inversion; metric geometry with those not changed by displacements; Euclidean geometry with those unchanged by Euclidean displacements. Thus we can classify geometries according to the group of transformations which leave properties unchanged.

CHAPTER VII

SOLID GEOMETRY

131. *CO-ORDINATES.* In the elementary treatment of co-ordinate geometry in three dimensions we take three mutually perpendicular planes, and define the co-ordinates x, y, z of a point in space to be its distances from these three planes, with the convention that if the point be in the part of space on one specified side of the plane, that distance shall be regarded as positive, and if on the other side, as negative.

Thus in the figure, if a, b, c be the co-ordinates of P, those

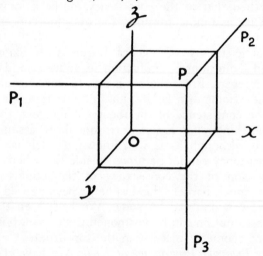

of its images P_1, P_2, P_3 in the co-ordinate planes are respectively $(-a, b, c)$, $(a, -b, c)$, $(a, b, -c)$, while its image in O has co-ordinates $(-a, -b, -c)$.

If I_1, I_2, I_3 be the operations of reflecting in the planes of yz, zx, xy respectively, then, if I denotes identity,

$I_1^2 = I_2^2 = I_3^2 = I$;

$I_2 I_3 = I_3 I_2$ is the operation of reflecting in the x-axis;

$I_1 I_2 I_3$ that of reflecting in the origin O.

Thus $(I_2I_3)^2 = I$, $(I_1I_2I_3)^2 = I$, which could also be deduced from the earlier relations.

132. *Surfaces and curves.* An equation between x, y, z denotes a surface, a locus of points whose co-ordinates satisfy the equation. A linear equation $ax + by + cz + d = 0$, where a, b, c, d are constants, represents a plane, for any point on the join of $P_1(x_1, y_1, z_1)$ and $P_2(x_2, y_2, z_2)$, has co-ordinates of form $(hx_1 + kx_2, hy_1 + ky_2, hy_1 + kz_2)$, where $h + k = 1$, and if the co-ordinates of P_1, P_2 satisfy the linear equation, so do the co-ordinates of the last point.

To get a representation for a curve, we may draw two surfaces through it, and write down their equations, but it will often be the case that the surfaces necessarily meet in another curve as well as in that given.

A line, however, *is* given by the equations of two planes which go through it.

133. *The "direction cosines"* of a line are the cosines of the angles that the line makes with the axes Ox, Oy, Oz; they are usually denoted by l, m, n.

If the line be the cut of the planes

$$a_1x + b_1y + c_1z + d_1 = 0, \quad a_2x + b_2y + c_2z + d_2 = 0,$$

the parallel line through O is the cut of planes with the same equations, except that d_1, d_2 vanish. The co-ordinates of any point on this parallel line satisfy:

$$x : y : z = b_1c_2 - b_2c_1 : c_1a_2 - c_2a_1 : a_1b_2 - a_2b_1,$$

and thus the direction cosines of the line are proportional to these quantities.

We always have $l^2 + m^2 + n^2 = 1$; and if (l, m, n), (l', m', n') be direction cosines of lines making an angle θ with each other, then

$$\cos 0 = ll' + mm' + nn'$$

If (x_1, y_1, z_1) be a point on a line whose direction cosines are l, m, n then any point on it has co-ordinates

$$(x_1 + lr, y_1 + mr, z_1 + nr)$$

for suitable r.

134. *"Quadrics"* are surfaces whose equations are of the second degree in x, y, z. Their shapes are most easily seen from the simplest equations of this kind.

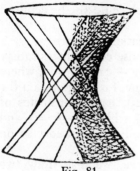

Fig. 81

The equation

The equation

$$\frac{x^2}{a^2} + \frac{y^2}{b^2} + \frac{z^2}{c^2} = 1$$

represents an *ellipsoid* whose "*principal semi-axes*" OA, OB, OC have lengths a, b, c. We get such a surface when a sphere is squashed in two directions, where the squashing in direction OC, say, is achieved by dividing all z-ordinates in a fixed ratio.

$$\frac{x^2}{a^2} + \frac{y^2}{b^2} - \frac{z^2}{c^2} = 1$$

represents a "*hyperboloid of one sheet*" (Fig. 81). If we rotate the hyperbola $x^2/a^2 - z^2/c^2 = 1$ round the z-axis, we get a hyperboloid of revolution, and a squashing parallel to the y-axis will furnish the required surface.

The equation

$$\frac{x^2}{a^2} - \frac{y^2}{b^2} - \frac{z^2}{c^2} = 1$$

represents a "*hyperboloid of two sheets*". If we rotate the hyperbola $x^2/a^2 - y^2/b^2 = 1$ round the x-axis, and squash parallel to the z-axis, we get the surface. Fig. 82 shews one half of the surface. The two kinds of hyperboloids and the ellipsoid are shewn all together in Fig. 85.

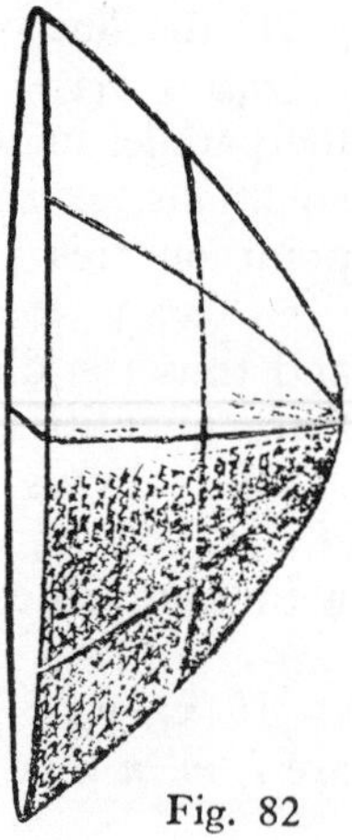

Besides these there are surfaces which correspond to parabolas, the "*elliptic paraboloid*", and the "*hyperbolic paraboloid*" with equations respectively.

Fig. 82

$$2x = y^2/b^2 + z^2/c^2 \quad \text{and} \quad 2x = y^2/b^2 - z^2/c^2.$$

The first can be obtained by squashing a paraboloid of revolution. The second would be obtained from the hyperboloid

of one sheet if the horizontal elliptical sections were pulled out
to be parabolas.

If AB, CD be intervals on two skew lines, divided into the
same number of equal parts, the joins of corresponding points
of division lie on a hyperbolic paraboloid.

"Degenerate" cases of quadrics are: (1) a pair of planes,
(2) a cone on a conic as base. Such a cone can always be cut,
by an appropriate plane, in a conic of any type, ellipse, parabola,
or hyperbola. A cone whose vertex is at the origin has an
equation homogeneous in x, y, z.

135. *Homogeneous Co-ordinates*. For further progress we
make our co-ordinates homogeneous, writing $x/w, y/w, z/w$ for
x, y, z. Then any plane has an equation of form

$$ax + by + cz + dw = 0, \qquad (1)$$

and $w = 0$ is the "*plane at infinity*". The "*co-ordinates*" of
plane (1) are a, b, c, d and only ratios are relevant. Any point
on the line through (x_1, y_1, z_1, w_1) with direction cosines
l, m, n, has co-ordinates of form $(x_1 + rl, y_1 + rm, z_1 + rn, w_1)$.
The point at infinity on the line is $(l, m, n, 0)$.

Generalizing this, as in the two-dimensional case, we take
a tetrahedron, and as co-ordinates of a point we take fixed
multiples of its distances from the faces of the tetrahedron.
Only the ratios of these co-ordinates are relevant.

If (x, y, z, w) and (x', y', z', w') are the co-ordinates of the
same point referred to two different tetrahedra, they are
connected by a linear transformation

$$x' = a_1 x + b_1 y + c_1 z + d_1 w$$
$$\cdots \cdots$$
$$w' = a_4 x + b_4 y + c_4 z + d_4 w \qquad (2)$$

Or, we may keep the tetrahedron of reference fixed, and look
on (x, y, z, w) and (x', y', z', w') as the co-ordinates of distinct
points P, P' satisfying (2). These equations then give a transformation of points into points, and if the determinant of the
coefficients is not zero, the transformation is a one-to-one
correspondence. If P describes a plane, so does P'; transformations with this property are called "*collineations*".

A collineation has, in general, four self-corresponding
points, and no more.

136. *Generators of Ruled Quadrics.* If in any system of homogeneous co-ordinates, $X = 0$, $Y = 0$ are the equations of two planes, then the plane $X + kY$ (i.e. the plane whose equation is $X + kY = 0$), goes through the line in which the planes X, Y cut, and we get any such plane by suitable choice of k.

Four planes through the line, with k_1, k_2, k_3, k_4 as their values of k, have the "*cross-ratio*"

$$(k_1 - k_2)(k_3 - k_4)/(k_2 - k_3)(k_4 - k_1).$$

This can be shewn to be independent of the base planes X, Y. (Cf. § 43). The planes cut any line in four points with this same cross-ratio.

A set of planes through a line is called a "*pencil*". If we have two pencils of planes $X + kY$, $Z + kW$, and we make planes with the same k correspond, the pencils are put into "*projective correspondence*", the cross-ratios of any four being equal to the cross-ratio of the corresponding four. A pair of corresponding planes cut in a line, and these lines lie on the surface whose equation is found, by eliminating k, to be $XW - YZ = 0$. This is of the second degree, if the two lines, which are axes of the pencils, are skew; the surface is then a hyperboloid of one sheet.

If our planes X, Y, Z, W are respectively
$x/a - z/c = 0$, $1 + y/b = 0$, $1 - y/b = 0$, $x/a + z/c = 0$,
the equation of the surface is

$$x^2/a^2 + y^2/b^2 - z^2/c^2 = 1.$$

We get the same equation if our planes are respectively
$x/a - z/c = 0$, $1 - y/b = 0$, $1 + y/b = 0$, $x/a + z/c = 0$.
This illustrates the fact that, on a hyperboloid of one sheet, there are two sets of lines, called "*generators*"; each set contains an infinite number of lines; any two lines in the same set are skew; any two in distinct sets intersect. The generators are indicated in Figs. 81, 85.

The lines in one set constitute a "*regulus*", the two reguli are "*opposite*". Surfaces with an infinite number of lines on them are called "*ruled surfaces*". Thus a ruled quadric is a hyperboloid of one sheet.

137. We can also reach a ruled quadric by way of its generators. If two skew lines be given in space, a line can be drawn through any point P to cut both. For draw a plane through P and one of the lines, and then join P to the point where this plane cuts the other line.

If then we have three skew lines, we can draw a line through each point on one to cut the other two. This gives an infinite number of lines cutting all three, and the set constitutes a regulus; the opposite regulus consists of all lines cutting this set.

The facts can be stated in another way. If three skew lines, 1, 2, 3 each cut three other skew lines $1'$, $2'$, $3'$, and we draw another line $4'$ to cut 1, 2, 3, and another line 4 to cut $1'$, $2'$, $3'$, then 4, $4'$ cut. The interesting thing, from the point of view of projective geometry, is that this fact can be shewn from the projective axioms provided Pappus' theorem be assumed. Conversely, if we assume this fact and the projective axioms, except

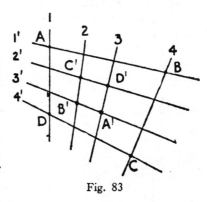

Fig. 83

Pappus' theorem, then the latter can be proved.

In the figure, $ABA'B'$, and $CDC'D'$ are a pair of Möbius tetrahedra (p. 27); for example, A, B, A', B' are on planes $DC'D'$, $C'D'C$, $D'CD$, CDC' respectively.

If $PQ'RP'QR'$ be a hexagon on a ruled quadric, such that PQ', $R\overset{\frown}{P}'$, QR', are generators of one regulus and $Q'R$, $P'Q$, $R'P$ generators of the opposite regulus, then PP', QQ', RR' concur; a generalization of Brianchon's theorem (§ 79).

138. *Tangents.* The tangent lines to an ellipsoid at a point lie in a plane, the "*tangent plane*" at the point, and this plane meets the ellipsoid at that point only. The tangent lines to a ruled quadric at a point also lie in a plane, but this tangent plane *cuts* the quadric in the two generators through the point.

A plane parallel to the tangent plane cuts the quadric in a hyperbola which gradually tends to a line-pair as the plane tends to the tangent plane. When a point moves along a generator, the tangent plane, at the point, turns round the generator and cuts the quadric again, at each position, in a generator of the opposite regulus.

139. *Imaginary points,* If we allow points with complex co-ordinates, the difference mentioned between a ruled quadric and an ellipsoid, or hyperboloid of two sheets, disappears. The sphere with centre $(0, 0, h)$, which touches the xy plane, has equation $x^2 + y^2 + (z - h)^2 = h^2$, and the points common to the sphere and the plane satisfy either $x + iy = 0$, or $x - iy = 0$. Thus the sphere cuts its tangent plane in the isotropic lines of that plane, and these may be regarded as generators of the sphere.

Introducing homogeneous co-ordinates, we may consider the cut of a sphere
$$(x - aw)^2 + (y - bw)^2 + (z - cw)^2 = r^2 w^2$$
and the plane at infinity, $w = 0$. This sphere, and hence all spheres, pass through the points where the plane at infinity meets the *"isotropic cone"*, $x^2 + y^2 + z^2 = 0$. These points constitute the *"circle at infinity"*, which corresponds to the point-pair $I, \mathcal{J}$ in the plane case.

Perpendicular lines, intersecting or not, cut the plane at infinity in points conjugate for the circle at infinity.

140. *Poles and polars for a quadric.* The main features of this very simple theory can be grasped from the case of the sphere (§ 25); the methods of projective geometry give the proofs of the general theorems.

If a line through a point P cuts a quadric in A, B, and Q be the harmonic conjugate of P for A, B, then P, Q are *"conjugate"* for the quadric. As the line through P varies, Q describes the *"polar plane"* of P; P is the *"pole"* of the plane; if tangent lines (real or imaginary) be drawn through P to the quadric, they lie on a quadric cone touching the quadric on its cut with the polar plane.

If P describes a line, then Q describes its *"polar line"*, through which pass all the polar planes of P as P moves.

If PP', $P'Q$, QQ', $Q'P$ be generators of a ruled quadric, PQ and $P'Q'$ are polar lines.

A tetrahedron $ABCD$ is "*self-polar*" for a quadric if each vertex is the pole of the opposite face. Referred to such a tetrahedron, the quadric has an equation of form
$$ax^2 + by^2 + cz^2 + dw^2 = 0.$$

If $ABCD$ be any tetrahedron, P any point in space, let AP cut the plane BCD in Q, and on AP take P' so that P, P' separate A, Q harmonically; then the transformation from P to P' is a "*harmonic homology*". (Cf. § 83.) Again, if through P we draw a line to cut AB, CD in R, S, and now take P' so that P, P' separate R, S harmonically, then the transformation from P to P' is a "*biaxial involution*".

Thus the tetrahedron gives four harmonic homologies I_1, I_2, I_3, I_4 and three biaxial involutions, say I_{23}, I_{31}, I_{12}; the squares of each of these are, of course, identity, and we may arrange the notation so that $I_{23} = I_2 I_3 = I_3 I_2$, and so on. We have a projective generalization of § 131, and indeed $I_1 I_2 I_3 = I_4$.

All these transformations leave invariant any quadric for which $ABCD$ is a self-polar tetrahedron. Further, and this is very important, any collineation, which leaves a quadric invariant and does not interchange its two reguli, is the product of two biaxial involutions.

141. *Pencils of quadrics.* Take two ellipsoids with the principal axes along the same three lines, one ellipsoid rather long in the z-direction, and the other squat and broad. They will cut in two curves shaped like bent pennies, which together form a "quartic" curve, i.e. one of the fourth order, since a plane may cut it in four points, but not more. Any two quadrics in general position cut in such a curve, real or imaginary.

A general equation, homogeneous of the second degree in x, y, z, w, will contain ten terms, viz. terms in
$$x^2, y^2, z^2, w^2, yz, zx, xy, xw, yw, zw,$$
By suitable choice of co-ordinates it can always be reduced to one of the forms mentioned in § 134.

At present we wish to note that as there are ten coefficients in the general equation, and only their ratios matter, we can draw at least one quadric, and in general only one, through *nine* given points.

If U, V be quadrics in general position, then $U + kV$ (k constant), is a quadric through the quartic curve in which U, V cut; if we vary k, we get a "*pencil*" of quadrics. If W be a quadric not in that pencil, then by an algebraical theorem, U, V, W cut in eight points, and any quadric of form $U + kV + k'W$ (k,k' constants), goes through these eight points; these quadrics form a "*net*".

Now nine points, in general, determine a quadric through them; take seven of them at seven of the eight cuts of U, V, W and two elsewhere not on U, V or W. Then k, k' can be found.

Hence all quadrics through seven points go through an eighth.

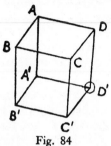

Fig. 84

For example, let A, B, C, D and A', B', C' be respectively on two plane cuts of an ellipsoid, and suppose A, B, A', B' lie in a plane and that B, C, B', C' lie in a plane. Then the plane-pairs $ABCD$, $A'B'C'$, and $ABA'B'$, $CC'D$, and $BCB'C'$, $AA'D$ form quadrics through seven points A, B, C, D, A', B', C' on the ellipsoid. Hence the planes $A'B'C'$, $AA'D$, $CC'D$ meet in a point D' on the ellipsoid.

If the quadric be a sphere, we have the six-circles theorem (§§ 18, 26), if we consider the cuts of the sphere and the planes.

142. *Confocal Quadrics.* Return to ordinary Cartesians, and consider the quadrics

$$\frac{x^2}{a - \lambda} + \frac{y^2}{b - \lambda} + \frac{z^2}{c - \lambda} = 1 \quad (a > b > c),$$

as λ varies.

If λ is positive or negative, but less than c, we have an ellipsoid in which the z-axis shrinks, as λ approaches c from below; the ellipsoid tends to flatten to the ellipse

$$\frac{x^2}{a - c} + \frac{y^2}{b - c} = 1, \quad z = 0.$$

When λ increases from c to b, then $a - \lambda$, $b - \lambda > 0$, $c - \lambda < 0$, and we have a ruled quadric which, when λ is just greater than c, has a very small z-axis, and when λ is near b, a very small y-axis, but a finite z-axis. The quadric tends to flatten to the hyperbola

$$\frac{x^2}{a - b} + \frac{z^2}{c - b} = 1, \ y = 0.$$

When λ increases from b to a, then $a - \lambda > 0$, $b - \lambda < 0$, $c - \lambda < 0$, and we have a hyperboloid of two sheets, which, as λ tends to a, has an x-axis tending to zero.

The two conics mentioned are called *"focal conics"*. They lie in perpendicular planes; the hyperbola has its vertices at the foci of the ellipse; the ellipse has its vertices at the foci of

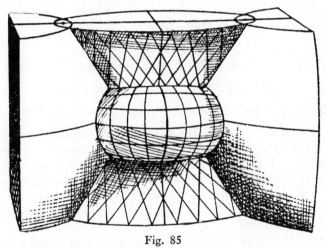

Fig. 85

the hyperbola. Each conic is the locus of vertices of cones of revolution on the other as base.

Through each point of space go three of these confocals, viz., an ellipsoid and a hyperboloid of each kind, and they cut orthogonally, that is, their tangent planes at a point of intersection are mutually perpendicular. Thus by means of confocals, we can partition space into boxes with curved faces, one pair of opposite faces being pieces of ellipsoids, the others, pieces of hyperboloids of one, or of two sheets.

143. *Quadric Envelopes.* So far we have considered quadrics as loci; we may equally well consider them as envelopes of a plane (l, m, n, r) in homogeneous co-ordinates. The equation of the quadric is then a homogeneous quadratic in l, m, n, r. Tangent planes to a (non-degenerate) quadric locus give the quadric as a quadric envelope.

In space, a point and a plane are dual elements, and we have: A quadric, and, in general, just one quadric, can be drawn to touch nine given planes. All quadrics which touch seven given planes, touch an eighth. These are the duals of theorems given in § 141.

If $\Sigma_1 = 0, \Sigma_2 = 0$ be quadric envelopes, then $\Sigma_1 + k\Sigma_2 = 0$ touches all their common tangent planes.

The plane (l, m, n, r) touches

$$\frac{x^2}{a - \lambda} + \frac{y^2}{b - \lambda} + \frac{z^2}{c - \lambda} = 1,$$

if $\qquad (a - \lambda)l^2 + (b - \lambda)m^2 + (c - \lambda)n^2 = r^2$

or if $\quad (al^2 + bm^2 + cn^2 - r^2) - \lambda(l^2 + m^2 + n^2) = 0.$

Thus if $al^2 + bm^2 + cn^2 = r^2$ is a given quadric envelope, the quadrics confocal to it, touch all the (imaginary) tangent planes which it has in common with $l^2 + m^2 + n^2 = 0$; the latter is the envelope equation of the circle at infinity, since it is the condition that $lx + my + nz = 0$ should touch $x^2 + y^2 + z^2 = 0$. This is the best method of approach to confocal quadrics.

144. *Projective generation of quadrics and cubic surfaces.* We now pass to projective geometry. We saw that two projective pencils of planes, with skew axes, generate a ruled quadric by the cuts of corresponding planes; but not every quadric in real space is ruled.

We now give a projective generation which will give any quadric, even in real space.

The set of all lines and planes through a point is called a "*bundle*", of which the point is the "*centre*". The planes of the bundle which go through a fixed line (through the centre), form a "*pencil*" of planes (§ 136); the lines of the bundle which lie in a plane (through the centre), form a "*pencil*" of lines, as in Chap. IV.

Two bundles of lines with the same or distinct centres can be put into "*projective correspondence*" with each other. This is a one-to-one correspondence such that if a line in one bundle describes a pencil in that bundle, the corresponding line in the other bundle describes a projective pencil. The correspondence is determined when four lines, no three coplanar, of one bundle, are matched with four such lines of the other. (If we cut the bundles by a plane, we have a projective correspondence between points on the plane.)

Similarly two bundles of planes can be put into projective correspondence, a pencil of planes in one corresponding to a pencil in the other.

Likewise a bundle of lines and a bundle of planes, a pencil of lines in the first corresponding to a projective pencil of planes in the second, the cross-ratio of any four of its lines being equal to the cross-ratio of the corresponding four planes.

After this introduction we can now give a projective generation of quadrics: if we have a bundle of lines and a projective bundle of planes, with distinct centres, the locus of the cuts of corresponding elements is a quadric through the centres. Any non-degenerate quadric can be generated in this way and the centres may be taken at any two points on it. If the line joining the centres lies on its corresponding plane, the quadric is a plane-pair.

Now take *three* projective bundles of planes in general position, that is, three corresponding planes must not, in general, meet in a line, and a plane through two centres must not correspond to a plane through the same two centres; then the locus of the cut of three corresponding planes is a *cubic* surface, with an equation of the *third* degree.

Algebraically we can take the equations of the bundles of planes to have forms:

$$kA + lB + nC = 0, \quad k'A' + l'B' + n'C' = 0,$$
$$k''A'' + l''B'' + n''C'' = 0$$

where $A = 0, \ldots, C'' = 0$ are the equations of planes, and
$k, \ldots, n''$ constants, and corresponding planes satisfy
$$k : l : n = k' : l' : n' = k'' : l'' : n''.$$
Eliminate the constants, and we have the equation of a cubic
surface, since the equation is of the *third* degree.

145. *The twisted cubic.* Two quadrics, as we saw, meet in
general in a quartic curve. Suppose however the quadrics were
ruled, and had a common generator l. Then one can be
generated by the cuts of corresponding planes of two pencils
of planes with axes l and, say, m_1; the second quadric can be
generated similarly from pencils with axes l and m_2, say. The
cuts of corresponding planes of all three pencils have a curve
as locus, which with l constitutes the complete cut of the two
quadrics.

The curve is a *"twisted cubic"*; a plane may meet it in three
points, but not in more.

146. *The double-six.* All quadrics in complex space, and
some in real space have an infinite number of lines lying on
them. But the general cubic surface in complex (or real),
space has not an infinite number of lines lying on it, though
some special cubic surfaces have. However, the general cubic
surface in complex space has just 27 lines on it; in real space
the number may be 3, 7, 15, 27. (The proof of such results as
this is not easy.) We consider the case of 27 lines, these are
done up into sets of what are called *"double sixes"*—there are
36 such sets—and it is such a set rather than the 27 lines which
we will consider further.

We saw that an infinite number of lines can be drawn to
meet three skew lines, and that they lie on a quadric. A fourth
skew line will meet the quadric in two points, real or imaginary,
usually distinct. Through each of these goes a generator of the
regulus opposite to that which contains the first three lines.
Hence, in general, there are just *two* lines which cut *four skew*
lines.

Let five skew lines 2, 3, 4, 5, 6 cut a line 1′; then 3, 4, 5, 6,
will be cut by another line 2′, say; 2, 4, 5, 6 will be cut by
another line besides 1′, call it 3′. Define 4′, 5′, 6′ similarly.

The theorem of the double-six asserts that 2′, 3′, 4′, 5′, 6′

have a common cutting line, which call 1. We have then two sets of six lines, 1, ... 6 and 1', ... 6', and if we call r, r' mates, each line of one set cuts all lines of the other set, except its mate.

It is such double-sixes as this that lie on the cubic surface.

146. *Line Co-ordinates.* In the most obvious treatment of geometry, space is considered to be made up of points; the principle of duality shews that there is an equivalent treatment when we suppose it is made up of planes. Plücker (1865) developed the idea of taking other elements as basic. We first consider the line.

How many co-ordinates fix a line? A line is given by its cuts with two parallel planes; each cut involves two co-ordinates, thus a line needs four. Those suggested are awkward, and lines parallel to the planes escape. We take another way.

If P_1, P_2 be points on the line with homogeneous co-ordinates (x_1, y_1, z_1, w_1) and (x_2, y_2, z_2, w_2), let

$$L = y_1 z_2 - y_2 z_1, \quad M = z_1 x_2 - z_2 x_1, \quad N = x_1 y_2 - x_2 y_1,$$
$$l = x_1 w_2 - x_2 w_1, \quad m = y_1 w_2 - y_2 w_1, \quad n = z_1 w_2 - z_2 w_1.$$

These six quantities are not independent, since $Ll + Mm + Nn$ vanishes identically, but their ratios, when the identical condition holds, fix a line uniquely. No lines escape.

In homogeneous Cartesians, we can take $w_1 = w_2 = 1$; then we have $l : m : n = x_1 - x_2 : y_1 - y_2 : z_1 - z_2$. Thus l, m, n are proportional to the direction cosines.

It is easily proved that the condition that the lines (L, M, N, l, m, n) and (L', M', N', l', m', n') meet is

$$Ll' + Mm' + Nn' + L'l + M'm + N'n = 0.$$

147. *The linear line-complex and the null-system.* When the point is taken as the element of space, we have loci; and when the plane, envelopes. What do we get when the line is taken as element?

The simplest structure is given if the co-ordinates of the line are subject to a linear relation

$aL + bM + cN + a'l + b'm + c'n = 0$ $(a, \ldots, \; c'$ constants). (1)

Lines satisfying such an equation constitute a *"linear complex"*.[*]

* The word "complex" here has nothing to do with "complex number".

We will approach this another way. If (p, q, r, s) be the co-ordinates of a plane, and (x, y, z, w) those of a point, consider the following transformation which makes a plane correspond to a point.

$$
\begin{aligned}
p &= \qquad\quad a_{12}y + a_{13}z + a_{14}w, \\
q &= a_{21}x \qquad\ + a_{23}z + a_{24}w, \\
r &= a_{31}x + a_{32}y \qquad\ + a_{34}w, \\
s &= a_{41}x + a_{42}y + a_{43}z
\end{aligned}
\qquad (2)
$$

where $a_{ij} = -a_{ji}, (i, j = 1, \ldots, 4)$ \qquad\qquad (3)

Since $a_{ij} = -a_{ji}$, it will be found that a point P always lies on its corresponding plane π. The point P is called the *"null-point"* of π, and π is its *"null-plane"*. The system of points and planes so connected is a *"null-system"*.

If a point Q be taken on the null-plane π of P, it can be 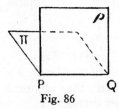 shewn that the null-plane ρ of Q (which goes through Q), goes through P. In general π, ρ are distinct, and hence cut in PQ. When Q moves along PQ, its null-plane turns round PQ.

Fig. 86

Now take homogeneous Cartesians; the plane at infinity has its null-point on it. Take this as the end of the z-axis, and for the xy-plane take any plane perpendicular to the z-axis. Take the null-point of the xy-plane as origin.

To the point $(0, 0, 1, 0)$ at the "end" of the z-axis corresponds the plane $(a_{13}, a_{23}, 0, a_{43})$, and as this is the plane at infinity $(0, 0, 0, 1)$, we have $a_{13} = a_{23} = 0$.

To the origin $(0, 0, 0, 1)$ corresponds the plane $(a_{14}, a_{24}, a_{34}, 0)$, and as this is the xy-plane $(0, 0, 1, 0)$, we have $a_{14} = a_{24} = 0$.

Hence our transformation turns the point (x', y', z', w') into the plane $(a_{12}y', a_{21}x', a_{34}w', a_{43}z')$,

or $\qquad\quad a_{12}(y'x - x'y) + a_{34}(w'z - z'w) = 0$,

or $\qquad\qquad y'x - x'y + k(z' - z) = 0$,

when we write $\ k = -a_{34}/a_{12}, \ w = w' = 1$.

To the point $(0, y', 0)$, in ordinary Cartesians, corresponds

$z/x = y'/k$, which is a plane through the y-axis at an angle $\alpha = \tan^{-1} y'/k$ to the xy-plane.

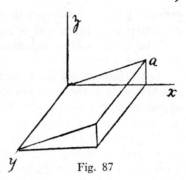

Fig. 87

As our y-axis may be any line which cuts the z-axis at right angles, we can now construct the null-plane of any point not on the z-axis. The null-planes of the latter points are perpendicular to the z-axis. The z-axis is the *"axis"* of the null-system.

We now shew that those lines of a linear complex which go through a point, lie in a plane. If a line through (x', y', z'), with direction cosines (l, m, n) satisfy (1), then (x, y, z) being any point on the line, we have

$$a(yz' - z'y) + b(zx' - z'x) + c(xy' - x'y)$$
$$+ a'(x - x') + b'(y - y') + c'(z - z') = 0$$

which represents a plane, whose co-ordinates p, q, r, s are given by equations like (2), satisfying (3), namely, restoring w,

$$p = cy' - bz' + a'w, \text{ and so on.}$$

Thus those lines of a linear complex, which go through a point, lie in a plane which is the null-plane of the point for a certain null-system. As the converse is obvious, we get a linear complex, if in Fig. 87 we draw through each point all lines in its null-plane.

When a point describes a line g, not in the complex, the corresponding null-planes all go through another line g_1, the *"conjugate"* of g. The axis of the null-system, and g, g_1 are met by a line perpendicular to them all.

If, in equation (1), the coefficients a', b', c', a, b, c were themselves proportional to the co-ordinates L', M', N', l', m', n' of a line, all lines satisfying (1) would meet this line: we then have a *"special"* complex, the condition for it being

$$aa' + bb' + cc' = 0.$$

148. *The linear congruence.* The lines, whose equations satisfy two such equations as (1), constitute a *"linear con-*

gruence"; it can be shewn that these consist of all lines which meet two fixed lines, real or imaginary, called the "*directrices*".

The lines, whose equations satisfy *three* such equations, constitute a regulus.

149. *Illustrations from statics.* Forces along two lines can balance, only if the lines coincide and the forces are equal and opposite; forces along three lines only if the lines are coplanar and concurrent, and the forces have suitable magnitudes.

If (suitable) forces along four lines balance, the lines lie on a regulus, since any line, which meets three of them, must meet the fourth; similarly for five and six forces, the lines must lie in a linear congruence, or in a linear complex, respectively.

Any system of forces can be reduced to a force and a couple in a plane perpendicular to the line of the force; the lines round which the system has zero moment, constitute a linear complex, and if any line be taken, not in the complex, the system can be reduced to a force along that line and one along the line conjugate to it for the complex.

150. *Projective Treatment.* If we have two projective pencils of lines in distinct planes, with distinct centres, and three pairs of corresponding lines meet, all such pairs meet. The pencils are "*in perspective*".

Suppose next, the centres are distinct points on the cut of the planes, and that cut is a self-corresponding line. The set of lines which meet distinct corresponding lines is then a linear complex.

150*a*. We can define a "*collineation*" in space as we did in the plane, p. 77. It only needs four variables (x, y, z, t) instead of three (x, y, z). This transformation turns planes into planes. Figures related by a non-degenerate collineation are "*projectively equivalent*". Examples are, two non-degenerate quadrics, two non-special linear complexes, two twisted cubics.

CHAPTER VIII

DIFFERENTIAL GEOMETRY IN SPACE

WE now use the differential calculus to find properties of curves and surfaces, and we shall be interested mainly in local properties, that is, those in the neighbourhood of a point.

151. *Curves.* We shall suppose the equations of a curve are given in the form:

$$x = f_1(t), \ y = f_2(t), \ z = f_3(t), \tag{1}$$

where t is a parameter, which we may think of as the time.

Thus, for example, $x = t$, $y = t^2$, $z = t^3$, gives a twisted cubic, and in fact, every twisted cubic (§ 145) is projectively equivalent to this.

We shall always assume that the functions of t in (1) are continuous, and possess all the continuous derivatives we need. If a point describes the curve (1), the components of its velocity are $f'_1(t), f'_2(t), f'_3(t)$, where a dash denotes the derivative. The direction cosines of the tangent to the curve at the point t are proportional to these components.

If P, Q, R be points on the curve, and we make Q move along the curve to P, the line PQ will tend to the position of the tangent at P. If Q, R both move along the curve to P, the plane PQR will tend to what is called the *"osculating plane"* at P. This plane contains the directions of velocity and of acceleration of the point at P.

The plane through P perpendicular to the tangent there is called the *"normal plane"* at P. It is perpendicular to the osculating plane and cuts it in the *"principal normal"* n, to the curve. The perpendicular at P to the osculating plane is the *"binormal,"* b.

Consider, for example, a screw

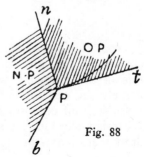

Fig. 88

motion round the z-axis. This will turn the point $(a, 0, 0)$ into a point with co-ordinates of form

$$x = a \cos t, \; y = a \sin t, \; z = bt,$$

for the first two equations express the result of rotating round an angle t, while the third represents a translation of amount bt parallel to the z-axis.

The point (x, y, z) describes a *"helix"*; the tangent at t has direction cosines proportional to $-a \sin t$, $a \cos t$, b. We may remark that the normal plane at any point P of the helix is the null-plane of P in a certain null-system.

This example shews that we have two sorts of curvature to consider, one of which is a kind of twist, depending on how fast the binormal varies. This is called the *"torsion"*.

We can follow the facts most easily if we consider the *"spherical representation"* of a curve. Take a fixed sphere of unit radius, and through its centre O, draw radii OT, OB parallel respectively to the tangent and binormal at P. Then if P describes a small arc of the curve, the ratio of this arc to that described by T is the *"radius of curvature"* ρ, and its ratio to that described by B is the *"radius of torsion"* τ.

The most important result is the Serret-Frenet formulæ. These are equivalent to the statement: As P moves on the curve, with constant speed, the trigon OT, ON, OB turns round O with a certain angular velocity; if this be resolved into angular velocities round these three axes, the components are $1/\tau$, 0, $1/\rho$ respectively. (ON is drawn parallel to the normal at P).

For our helix we find:

$$\frac{1}{\rho} = \pm \frac{a}{a^2 + b^2}, \; \frac{1}{\tau} = \frac{b}{a^2 + b^2}.$$

152. *Surfaces.* To fix the position of a point on the earth's surface, we may give its latitude and longitude. We can look at this in the following way: Take two curves on the sphere, namely the equator and the Greenwich meridian, and along these step off equal distances, as we should if we were using Cartesian axes in a plane. Through points on the equator, draw meridians; through points on the Greenwich meridian,

draw parallels of latitude. The position of a point on the earth's surface is then given by the two curves, one of each family, which go through it. Thus each point, except the poles, acquires two definite co-ordinates.

We can generalize this method to any surface, or rather to a piece of any surface; we take two families of curves on the surface, such that through each point goes just one curve of each family, so that two of the same family never meet, as if a fine fishing-net were thrown over the surface. Take some point O on the surface as origin, and call the curve of one family through O, the u-axis, the curve of the other family, the v-axis. Through any other point P on the (piece of the) surface goes a curve of each family; one meets the u-axis at a point at distance a, say, from O, the other meets the v-axis at a point at distance b, say, from O, these distances being measured *along the axes*. Then P is given the co-ordinates (a, b).

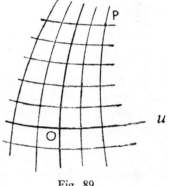

Fig. 89

Instead of using the actual distances a, b, we could use any continuous functions of them, with continuous positive derivatives.

The curves of our families are then $u = $ const., and $v = $ const.

If we suppose our surface is immersed in ordinary space with rectangular axes x, y, z, it will be given if we know x, y, z at each point (u, v) of the surface, say

$$x = f_1(u, v), \; y = f_2(u, v), \; z = f_3(u, v);$$

we suppose always that, on the piece considered, these f_i are continuous functions of u, v with continuous derivatives in u, v of as high an order as we need. The surface is then *"regular"* at (u, v) and, in particular, has a definite tangent plane there.

"*Singular*" points, where this is not the case, will not usually be considered. Thus we have

$$dx = \frac{\delta f_1}{\delta u} du + \frac{\delta f_1}{\delta v} dv,$$

$$dy = \frac{\delta f_2}{\delta u} du + \frac{\delta f_2}{\delta v} dv,$$

$$dz = \frac{f_3}{\delta u} du + \frac{\delta f_3}{\delta v} dv,$$

Hence the square ds^2 of the distance between the points (x_1, y_1, z_1) and $(x_1 + dx, y_1 + dy, z_1 + dz)$ of this surface is

$$dx^2 + dy^2 + dz^2$$

$$= \left(\frac{\delta f_1}{\delta u} du + \frac{\delta f_1}{\delta v} dv\right)^2 + \dots + \dots$$

$$= E\ du^2 + 2F\ du\ dv + G\ dv^2$$

where E, F, G are functions of u, v, whose form we need not here consider. We regard ds as measured on the surface.

Take, for example, the sphere, u being the co-latitude, v the longitude, then

$$x = a\ \sin u\ \cos v, \quad y = a\ \sin u\ \sin v, \quad z = a\ \cos u,$$
satisfy
$$x^2 + y^2 + z^2 = a^2.$$

Forming differentials, squaring and adding, we get

$$dx^2 + dy^2 + dz^2 = a^2\ \sin^2 u\ dv^2 + a^2 du^2.$$

The "*normal*" to a surface at a point P is the perpendicular at P to the tangent plane at P.

153. *Contour lines.* To describe the shape of a surface near a point, move the surface round until the tangent plane at the point is horizontal. If the surface be regarded as a tract of country the point might be, for example, a *summit*, higher than all neighbouring points, or the *bottom of a valley*, lower than all neighbouring points. The distinction between these is of no consequence for us, but we must distinguish between a *summit* and a *pass* between two or more hills. From a pass we may descend to lower ground or climb a hill.

Near most points of a surface, the surface resembles a quadric; near a summit S it is like an ellipsoid, and the contour lines near S are approximately ellipses. Draw a normal to the surface at S; with our position for the surface, this is vertical. Through it draw vertical planes to cut the surface. As the plane turns round the normal, the curvature *

Fig. 90

at S of the section changes continuously and has a minimum when the section near S is a path of slowest descent, and a maximum when it is a path of steepest descent. These curvatures are called the "*principal curvatures*" at S, their centres the "*principal centres of curvature*"; the corresponding planes go through the principal axes of the ellipse to which the contour lines approximate. They are called the "*principal planes*", and are at right angles.

There is an exceptional case when the curvatures of the sections are all equal; the contour lines then approximate to circles, and S is called an "*umbilic*".

That the above restriction on the form of the surface is not very severe, is clear if we take the tangent plane as the xy-plane and z as the depth of points of the surface. Its equation is then of the form

$$z = ax^2 + 2hxy + by^2 + \text{terms of higher order.}$$

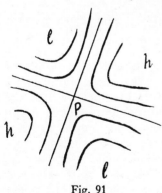

Fig. 91

Omitting the terms of higher order, which when x, y are small, are small compared with those retained, we have indeed a quadric.

Now suppose the point is a pass P between two hills. The contour lines are then arranged as in the figure; l is low country, h is high country. Through P go two paths which run level at P; their tangents at P are horizontal. These tangents are in the "*asymptotic directions*" at P, and the contour lines near P

---

* The "curvature" of a curve at a point is the inverse of its radius o curvature (§ 33). It is often more convenie nt than the latter.

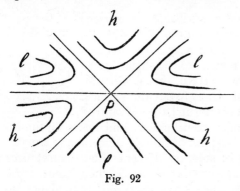

Fig. 92

resemble hyperbolas with asymptotes in these directions. Consider sections of the surface made by planes through the normal at P. If the plane goes through the low country, the section curves downward and the curvature at P is greatest when the plane bisects the angle between the asymptotic directions. If the plane goes through the high country, the section curves upward and the curvature at P is again greatest when the plane bisects the angle between the asymptotic directions. The planes giving these greatest curvatures are "*principal planes*", obviously at right angles; the principal curvatures are now given contrary signs.

At a usual point on the surface we thus have two "*principal directions*" defined by the principal planes. Suppose a point moves continuously on a surface, always in a principal direction at the point it has reached: it describes a "*line of curvature*"; if it moves continuously in an asymptotic direction, it describes an "*asymptotic line*".*

The osculating plane of an asymptotic line at any point is a tangent plane to the surface there.

There are, however, unusual points, though regular. We have mentioned the umbilics. From such a point a line of curvature proceeds in *each* direction. But there is another type of unusual point. If P were a pass with three nearby hills, the contour lines might be arranged as in the figure, and if we go from a piece of high country (h) through P to an opposite piece of low country (l), the path has a flex at P, the curvature vanishing there. P is then a "*parabolic point*". It may be isolated, as in this case, or such points may lie on a curve. For instance, consider a bell of the usual shape. At the upper

* It is a great pity that the word "line" and not "curve," is usual here: in the greater part of this book, "line" means "straight line."

part, the principal curvatures are in the same direction, near the mouth they are in contrary directions; a circle of parabolic points separates the two areas.

Or consider an anchor ring. At an inner point A the curvatures are contrary, at an outer point B they are in the same direction. If a plane touches the surface all along a circle (such as the plane of a table, if the ring rests on it), the circle is composed of parabolic points.

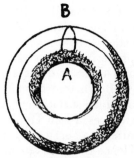

Fig. 93

154. *Illustrations of lines of curvature*. For a surface of revolution, the principal sections at a point are given by the plane through the axis, and the plane perpendicular to this plane through the normal to the profile at the point. For example, if we rotate a catenary about its directrix, we get a

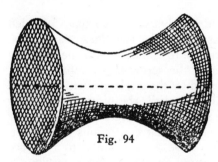

Fig. 94

"*catenoid*", and its two principal radii of curvature at a point P are (1) the distance from P to the directrix measured along the normal at P, (2) the radius of curvature of the catenary at P. These are equal and opposite for this particular surface (§34).

An interesting theorem of Dupin concerns three families of surfaces of such a kind that through each point of space, or of some portion of space, goes one surface of each family and further, such that surfaces of different families cut orthogonally; in this way space is partitioned into boxes with curved faces, cutting at right angles. Confocal quadrics furnish an instance of such families. Dupin's theorem states that the surfaces cut each other in their lines of curvature.

This leads to an unexpected theorem of Liouville. A transformation in a plane which turns points into points and which preserves angles, that is, which is such that the angle at which two curves cut equals that at which their transforms cut, is called "*conformal*". We already know that inversion has this property. But so have many other transformations in a plane, and their study is a part of function-theory.

But a transformation in space which preserves the angles at which surfaces cut, turns orthogonal surfaces into orthogonal surfaces. From Dupin's theorem it follows that lines of curvature on a surface become such lines on its transformed surface. Hence if *all* curves on a surface be lines of curvature, this will be the case for the transformed surface. But only spheres have this property. Thus the transformation turns spheres into spheres. It is never more complicated than the product of inversions in spheres. And that is Liouville's result.

155. *Torses.* If a curve be drawn on a surface, and normals to the surface be drawn at its points, they are usually skew lines, and they trace out a ruled surface, that is, one with an infinite number of lines on it.

A distinction has to be drawn between two types of ruled surface, not very easy to grasp. Consider two lines of a regulus, close together; we can move one to coincide with the other by means of a screw motion, and the screw has a definite *pitch*, defined as displacement divided by the angle of turn. For some types of ruled surfaces, called "*torses*", the pitch of the screw tends to zero when the two lines considered are taken closer and closer together. We then say that contiguous lines meet.

This latter case arises when we draw normals to a surface at points of a line of curvature on the surface; contiguous normals meet, and sketch out a torse, while their points of meeting lie on a twisted curve.

To illustrate this further, we will begin with a twisted curve, and take the helix. If we draw the tangents to the helix, and consider the half of each tangent which goes in a fixed direction of turn of the helix, these halves outline a portion of a torse. The backward halves outline the other portion. The complete torse bends at the helix, which is a sharp "*cuspidal edge*". An osculating plane of the helix touches the torse all along a tangent to the helix.

The most important property of a torse is that any piece of it can be continuously bent—or developed—into a piece of a plane. Thence torses are often called *"developable surfaces"*. All regular points of a torse, those not on its edge, are parabolic points; one principal curvature vanishes. Conversely, any surface, whose regular points are all parabolic, is a torse. Cones and cylinders are very special cases.

If a surface is ruled,* but is not a torse, its generators form one of the families of asymptotic lines; the other family of asymptotic lines consists of curves which cut the generators in projective ranges. This generalizes a property of the ruled quadric, in which both families are straight lines.

156. *Intrinsic Geometry.* We make a very important distinction between the geometry on a surface when it is regarded as immersed in space, and its intrinsic geometry, which deals with properties which can be treated on the surface without reference to the space which contains it.

We say a piece of surface is *"deformed"* or *"bent"* when it is continuously bent but not stretched or compressed, and thus the distance between two points of the surface, measured on the surface, is not changed, and when the surface remains regular at all its points during the bending. The intrinsic geometry of the original and the deformed surface do not differ; thus the intrinsic geometry of a torse is the same as that of a plane.

The principal curvatures at a point are not intrinsic, for they can obviously be altered by bending; but now comes a surprising fact: their product is intrinsic, it is *not* changed by bending. As the proof of this by analysis is not too easy, we give instead a geometrical definition of the *"total curvature"*, as the product of the principal curvatures is called.

Take a unit sphere and draw the radius parallel to the normal at a point P of the surface. The radius meets the sphere in the *"spherical representation"* of P. Clearly we must distinguish between the two sides of the surface, and draw the normal on a selected side. By this representation, to a curve on

* Through an arbitrary point on a general ruled surface goes *one* line which lies on the surface; for a ruled quadric, there are *two* such lines. Such lines are called *"generators"*.

the surface corresponds, in general, a curve on the sphere, and to a piece, a piece. But as normals to the surface at different points may be parallel, pieces on the sphere might overlap even when they correspond to non-overlapping pieces on the surface. But if we take pieces on the surface, not too large, this will not occur.

To a torse will correspond only a *curve* on the sphere, since the normals at all points of a generator are parallel to the binormal of the edge at the point where the generator meets the edge. But, in general, to a small piece round P on the surface will correspond a small piece on the sphere, and the ratio of the area of the latter to the area of the former, as these areas shrink to zero, tends to the total curvature at P. This is the geometrical definition promised.

The total curvature of a quadric at a point varies as the fourth power of the perpendicular from the centre to the tangent plane at the point.

157. *Geodesics.* If we take two points on a surface, not too far apart, the shortest arc joining them on the surface is called a *"geodesic"*, and this remains the shortest arc when the surface is bent. But for some surfaces if the points are too far apart, there may not be a unique arc joining them, which is shorter than all the others. Thus on a sphere, all meridians joining two poles have the same length.

If we stretch a string over a piece, not too large, of a surface, it lies along a geodesic arc, and simple statical considerations shew that the osculating plane of the arc, at each point, is normal to the surface at the point. This gives a step-by-step definition of a geodesic.

Suppose a geodesic from P *meets* another from P which begins in a slightly different direction. Then as we vary the direction at P continuously, the geodesics all touch an envelope QQ'. If R is on a geodesic from P, and between P and the envelope, then the arc PR is the shortest join of P, R; but if, for example the geodesic arc PRQ in the figure were shorter than the

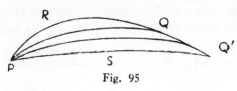

Fig. 95

geodesic arc PSQ', then by the properties of envelopes, the length of PSQ' is the sum of the lengths of PRQ and QQ', and as QQ' is longer than the geodesic from Q to Q', it follows that the arc PSQ' is not the shortest between P and Q'.

If the total curvature at each point of the surface is negative, that is, the principal curvatures are in opposite directions, this phenomenon cannot occur.

158. *Surfaces of constant curvature.* When a surface is bent, the element of arc-length ds is not changed. Further, if two pieces of surfaces can be put into one-to-one correspondence with each other so that ds at corresponding points agree (and the intrinsic geometries are therefore the same), then if the total curvature at each point is negative, we can vary the first piece continuously, with its tangent planes varying continuously, until each of its points coincides with the corresponding point of the second. If the total curvature is positive, the same is true, except that we may have to replace one piece by its mirror image.

Again, when a surface is bent, its total curvature at each point is unchanged. But it is not true, in general, that if two pieces correspond point by point so that the total curvatures at corresponding points, are equal, then one can be deformed into the other, or into the mirror image. This is however true when the total curvatures are *constant* over the pieces as well as equal.

This leads us to consider surfaces of constant total curvature K. If $K = 0$, at least one principal curvature vanishes; all points of the surface are parabolic, and we have a torse (or cone, or cylinder), which can be deformed to a plane.

A sphere is an obvious instance of a surface of constant positive curvature; and to appreciate its peculiar position among surfaces, we enlarge our theory. So far our work has referred to pieces, not too large, of a surface: it has been a *local* theory; there is a much more difficult *global* theory which considers the surface as a whole. It can be shewn that a complete closed surface (one without a boundary), which has constant positive curvature and is not a sphere, must have singular points. In other words, a sphere cannot be deformed without acquiring singular points, though a portion of a sphere, however nearly complete, can be so deformed.

Figs. 96, 97 shew two infinite surfaces of constant positive curvature.

A surface of constant negative curvature, without a boundary, must have singular points. The simplest is the *"pseudo-sphere"*, Fig. 98, obtained by rotating the tractrix

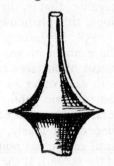

Fig. 96   Fig. 97   Fig. 98

Fig. 99

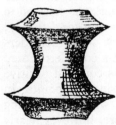

Fig. 100

round its directrix. It has a circle of cusps. Any regular piece of a surface with the same constant curvature can be bent to coincide with any regular piece of the pseudo-sphere. In particular, any regular piece of the pseudo-sphere can be fitted on to any other regular piece; if it is moved along or turned round in any way, it can be bent so that it still fits. In this respect the pseudo-sphere resembles the sphere, though in the latter, the fitting can be done without bending.

Figs. 99, 100 represent other surfaces of constant negative curvature.

The geometry and trigonometry on a sphere is like that on the plane in elliptic or spherical geometry. The geometry and trigonometry on a pseudo-sphere is like that on the hyperbolic plane. In both cases geodesics on the surface correspond to straight lines on the plane. As there is no surface without a boundary, and with constant negative curvature, which is regular at all its points, no surface in Euclidean space can represent the *whole* of the hyperbolic plane.

In the representations just given the distance between any pair of points equals that between the corresponding pair. If we drop this requirement, we can represent a piece of a surface of constant curvature on a Euclidean plane, so that geodesics correspond to straight lines; and this can be done only for surfaces of constant curvature. (Beltrami.)

The theory we have been considering is obviously connected with map-making, and it was the problems in that art that led to its creation.

The theorem above on the indeformability of spheres holds for any egg-shaped surface. In fact, any two such surfaces which can be deformed into one another are congruent. (Weyl.)

Another difficult theorem is that such a surface has at least three closed geodesics. A theorem of Bonnet's may also be mentioned: if the curvature of an egg-shaped surface exceeds $1/A^2$ everywhere, its maximum chord is less than πA.

159. *Geodesic Curvature.* If we draw any curve on a surface and then, at each point of the curve, the tangent plane to the surface, these envelop a torse, since they depend on one parameter only. When we develop the torse on to a plane, the curve becomes a plane curve, and its curvature at any point equals what is called the "*geodesic curvature*" of the curve on the surface at the corresponding point.

In spite of the way we have obtained it, the geodesic curvature of a curve at a point on a surface is an intrinsic property of the surface; it measures the rapidity with which the curve departs from a geodesic. The geodesic curvature of a geodesic itself is zero.

There is a remarkable connection between the geodesic curvatures ρ at points on a closed curve and the total curvature K of the surface at points of the piece enclosed by the curve. We will suppose the curve can be shrunk to a point continuously, without leaving the surface. If we divide the portion of the surface inside the curve into small pieces, and use the spherical representation of the surface, the value of K at a point is the ratio of the area of a small piece of the sphere to the area of the corresponding piece of the surface, in the limit when the areas tend to zero. If we call the integral of K over the interior of the curve, the *total curvature* of the surface over that interior, this total curvature equals the area of the corresponding piece of the sphere. Then it can be shewn that the sum of this total curvature and the integral of ρ round the curve equals 2π.

In particular, if K is constant on the surface, and we draw a triangle whose sides are geodesic arcs, we can deduce from this that the sum of the interior angles of the triangle minus K times its area equals π. Hence the area is the defect or excess of the angle-sum of the triangle divided by K, which shews again the analogy between the non-Euclidean geometries and the geometry on surfaces of constant curvature.

160. *Minimal Surfaces.* If a soap film be spread over a closed curved wire of any shape, it takes up a position such that its area is as small as possible in the circumstances. The condition for this is that the principal curvatures at each point are equal and opposite, and the same condition is necessary if we spread the film between two, or more, curves. These surfaces are called *"minimal surfaces"*.

For example, take two circular wires, of equal radii, placed one above the other in planes perpendicular to the join of their centres, and spread a film between them, but not over the rings. The film takes the form of a catenoid, Fig. 94, and this is the only minimal surface of revolution.

The only ruled minimal surface is the *"helicoid"* which resembles the common domestic screw. It is generated by a line, which cuts a fixed line at right angles, and moves by a screw motion of constant pitch round the fixed line as axis. It is remarkable that the helicoid is deformable into the catenoid; we can wrap it round the neck of the catenoid, its axis becoming the circle round the neck and its generators the meridians of the catenoid.

This deformability theorem is a case of one of much interest. A *general screw surface* is generated when any arc, plane or curved, is given a screw motion round an axis. Such a surface can always be deformed into one of revolution, the helices on it becoming parallel circles (Bour). In particular, if the screw surface is generated by a straight line which meets the axis at an angle, not a right angle, then it can be deformed to a ruled quadric of revolution by wrapping the axis round the neck of the quadric; the generators of the screw surface become generators of a regulus on the quadric.

Returning to minimal surfaces, the following properties are characteristic; the asymptotic lines at each point are at right angles; the spherical representation preserves angles unchanged.

There are even minimal surfaces with algebraic equations. Take two parabolas in perpendicular planes, each having its vertex at the focus of the other. The right bisector planes of all joins of points of one parabola to points of the other envelope such a minimal surface.

161. *Surfaces of constant mean curvature.* If a soap film be spread between two circular wires arranged as before, but the wires be covered by discs so that the pressure inside the film can be made to differ from that outside, then the film becomes a surface such that the sum of the principal curvatures at each point is constant.

The profile of such a surface, when it is a surface of revolution, is the locus of the focus of a conic which rolls along a straight line (the catenary is the locus of the focus of a parabola). The complete profile is either a curve with waves (Fig. 101) or loops (Fig. 102), and the soap film will shew only a portion of it. Biological illustrations will be found in D'Arcy Thompson's *Growth and Form.*

162. *The case of quadrics.* If OA, OB, OC

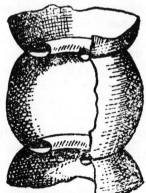

Fig. 101   Fig. 102

be the semi-axes of an ellipsoid in order of decreasing lengths, the plane AOB can be rotated round OB until it cuts the ellipsoid in a circle; for, as it rotates, the semi-axis of the section which is perpendicular to OB decreases from OA to OC. The image of the circular section, with respect to the plane AOB, is also a circular section; and all planes parallel to either of these planes of circular section give circular sections.

In fact, ellipsoids and both types of hyperboloids have two families of circular sections; in the case of the ellipsoid and the hyperboloid of two sheets, there are two tangent planes in each family, and they touch the surface in umbilics. Thus an ellipsoid has four umbilics; they are its cuts with the focal hyperbola; a hyperboloid of two sheets has four umbilics; they are its cuts with the focal ellipse.

Let P, Q be a pair of umbilics, not opposite, on an ellipsoid. Tie the ends of a string PRQ to P,Q, and stretch PR, RQ tight over the ellipsoid. These pieces then lie on geodesic arcs. If we put a pencil at R, and let it move over the ellipsoid in the same way as when an ellipse is described in a plane, then R will describe a line of curvature.

If we look at the figure of confocal quadrics (Fig. 85), it is obvious that we can fit straight lines in the space above the ellipsoid and inside the ruled quadric, so that the lines touch both these surfaces. We can move such a line so that its point of contact with the ellipsoid describes a *geodesic*, which wanders to and fro between the curves in which the ruled quadric cuts the ellipsoid. The point of contact on the ruled quadric also describes a geodesic on that surface.

163. *Deformation of surfaces.* In one simple case we can follow the deformation in detail. A ruled quadric can be deformed into a series of surfaces, the generators of one regulus on the quadric remaining straight while those of the other regulus bend. This statement concerns the whole of a surface. The rest of this section deals with pieces only.

A minimal surface can be deformed into a series of minimal surfaces, so that each point describes an ellipse, all the ellipses having the same centre.

As might be expected, though it is not easy to prove, a

surface of positive curvature becomes indeformable if an arc of a curve, not straight, on it, be kept rigid. The same is true for a surface of negative curvature, if the arc is not part of an asymptotic line; such a surface can be bent round an asymptotic line.

A ruled surface can be deformed in infinitely many ways so that a given curve becomes a plane curve; it can also be deformed so that a given geodesic on it, becomes straight. But if during a deformation one generator is kept straight, all remain straight, and the resulting surface is also ruled; there is just one such deformation which turns a given curve into an asymptotic line on the deformed surface.

Conversely, if two ruled surfaces correspond by a deformation, either the generators correspond, or each can be deformed into a ruled quadric, the generators of one surface becoming lines of one regulus, those of the other, lines of the opposite regulus.

164. *Congruence of lines.* If the normal be drawn at each point of a surface, we have a set of lines depending on two parameters, for example the parameters u, v which fix a point on the surface.

Generally a family of lines, each given by two parameters, and such that only a finite number go through a general point, is called a "*congruence*".

A congruence is a "*normal congruence*" if there is a surface normal to all lines of the congruence. There is then an infinite number of such surfaces. The rays of light streaming normally from a surface give an obvious instance and, by theorem of Malus and Dupin, if the rays are reflected or refracted at a surface, they still form a normal congruence. If a surface strikes a normal congruence at any angles, and the congruence be deformed with the surface, it remains a normal congruence (Beltrami).

Now consider any congruence of lines. In the congruence, take a particular line l, and the lines round it and close to it; if we draw the common perpendiculars to l and each of these lines, their feet on l fill up an interval; the ends of this interval, when the lines are very close, are the "*limiting*" points on l.

The corresponding common perpendiculars are themselves mutually perpendicular. Again on each line *l*, there are two points where it meets an "adjacent" line of the congruence; these are the *"foci"* of *l*. For instance, in the case of normals to a surface, as we move along a line of curvature, each normal meets the adjacent normal. For such a normal congruence, indeed, the foci and limiting points on any line coincide, but in general, the foci lie between the limiting points, the two pairs having the same mid-point.

Again, if we consider the normals to any surface, such as an ellipsoid, on each normal there are two centres of principal curvature. The locus of these centres is the *"central surface"*, and each normal touches this surface twice. For any congruence, we consider the locus of the foci of its lines; the lines of the congruence each touch this *"focal surface"* twice. They are also given as the sets of tangents to a single-infinity of curves on one sheet of the focal surface, and in the case of a normal congruence, these curves are geodesics on the surface.

The central surface of a congruence of normals to a given surface may be regarded as consisting of two sheets, each the locus of one principal centre of curvature. These are usually surfaces, but in exceptional cases, one or both may be curves.

If one of the sheets is a curve, all the normals meet it, and the given surface is the envelope of a sphere of varying radius whose centre describes the curve; the moving sphere cuts the sphere which is in a contiguous position, in a circle, and the "envelope" is the surface traced out by these circles. On the given surface one family of lines of curvature consists of circles.

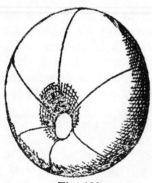

Fig. 103

If both sheets of the central surface are curves, it is remarkable that then these curves must be focal conics of a confocal system of quadrics, and any surface, to which the congruence of lines is normal, is a *"Dupin cyclide"*, the envelope of a sphere which touches three fixed spheres, each in assigned ways, internally or externally; but it is permissible to change *all* the ways simultaneously. The "envelope" of the sphere is explained above. Fig. 103 shews the envelope for the case of one internal, two external tangencies. Both families of lines of curvature on the cyclide are circles, and the cyclide is touched all along such a line by some sphere whose centre is on one of the focal conics.

Special cases of cyclides are the anchor ring, and the inverse of an anchor ring or of a quadric cone.

To appreciate the notion of the envelope of a moving sphere, consider the simple case of a sphere of constant radius whose centre moves on a circle of greater radius. All the spheres touch an anchor ring, and "contiguous" spheres cut in a circle which lies on the ring.

164*a*. It may be mentioned that although an egg-shaped surface is indeformable (p. 143) it becomes deformable if any portion, however small, be removed.

The classical theory of surfaces makes "differentiability" assumptions, *e.g.* that the surface has a unique tangent plane at each point which varies continuously with the point.

Recent work by Russian mathematicians A. D. Alexandrov, A. W. Pogurelov, and others reconstructs the theory, avoiding such assumptions, thus solving several outstanding problems.

CHAPTER IX

ALGEBRAIC PLANE CURVES

165. We take up the theory of algebraic plane curves at the point where we left it in Chap. II. We use those methods which we found so fruitful for conics: (1) We take homogeneous Cartesian or general homogeneous co-ordinates, (2) we allow points to have complex co-ordinates,* (3) we consider envelopes along with loci.

Thus to illustrate the first point, consider $y^2z = x^3$. If

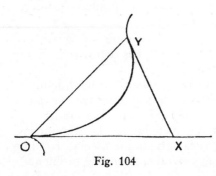

Fig. 104

we take $z = 0$ as the line at infinity (or put $z = 1$), we get $y^2 = x^3$, which has a cusp at $x = 0$, $y = 0$. If we take in turn $y = 1$, and $x = 1$, we get $z = x^3$, with a flex at Y, and $z = 1/y^2$, a curve with asymptotes XO, XY, if OY is regarded as the line at infinity.

Thus $y = x^3$ has an unsuspected cusp at infinity, and $y = 1/x^2$ has one inflectional asymptote, and one cuspidal asymptote.

166. *Simple singularities.* The singular points of an algebraic curve are of great importance. We consider the simplest first.

When a point, in describing a curve, passes through a node, it does not change its direction of motion, nor does the tangent change its sense of turning; but at a cusp, the point does change its direction of motion, though again the tangent does not change its sense of turning.

Now consider a curve as an envelope, described by its tangents. When the tangent passes through the position of a

* An isolated point will then be regarded as a node with imaginary tangents.

bitangent, it does not change its sense of turning, nor does its point of contact change the direction of its motion; *a bitangent is dual to a node.* When the tangent passes through the position of a tangent at a flex, the tangent changes its sense of turning, but the point of contact moves on; *a tangent at a flex is dual to a cusp.*

167. *Intersections of Cubics.* A curve in homogeneous co-ordinates will be represented by a homogeneous polynomial in x, y, z; if this is of degree n, the curve is of "*order n*", or is an "*n-ic*". A general line meets it in n points.

The number of distinct terms of the third degree is ten; namely those in x^3, y^3, z^3, y^2z, yz^2, z^2x, zx^2, x^2y, xy^2, xyz.

For the n-th degree, the number is $\frac{1}{2}(n + 1)(n + 2)$.

If a point be given on an n-ic, this gives one linear equation for the coefficients, and as only their ratios matter in the equation, we might expect that, if we are given

$$\tfrac{1}{2}(n + 1)(n + 2) - 1 = \tfrac{1}{2}n(n + 3)$$

points on an n-ic, the curve would be fixed, at least if the points were non-singular.

Thus nine points would fix a cubic curve ($n = 3$); and this would indeed be so, if they gave nine independent conditions. But this, we shall see, is not always the case.

A curve of order r cuts one of order s in rs points. In simple cases, this is easily shewn, but if we wish the statement to be universally true, we must take into account any common points at infinity, and, what is much harder, we must count properly the cuts at a point which is singular for one or both. We postpone that consideration.

Thus two cubics $C = 0$, $C' = 0$ in general position will cut in nine points ($r = s = 3$), and *all* cubics of form $C + kC' = 0$ (k constant), will go through these nine. Thus this set of nine points does *not* fix a cubic.

But eight of them, together with a fresh point, will do so, and the cubic through them will pass through the ninth common point of C, C'.

Hence we have shewn that *all cubics through eight points go* *through a ninth.* This theorem gives rise to a number of special cases, when the cubic is reducible.*

(1) It contains the Pivot theorem (Fig. 9), for the line $A'BC$ and the circle $AB'C'$ together constitute a cubic through A, B, C, A', B', C' and the circular points at infinity. So do the line $B'CA$ and the circle $BC'A'$; also the line $C'AB$ and the circle $CA'B'$. These cubics have a common point O.

(2) It contains Pascal's theorem (Fig. 46), for the lines $B'C$, $C'A$, $A'B$ constitute a cubic, so do the lines BC', CA', AB', and so does the conic $ABCA'B'C'$ together with the line DE. These cubics all go through A, B, C, A', B', C', D, E and hence have a common point F.

(3) The lines AB, DE, GH of Fig. 105 and the lines AD, BE, CF each constitute cubics through eight points A, B, C, D, E, F, G, H. Hence any cubic through them goes through the cut X, of CF, HG.

(4) Let B move along the curve to A, and E move to D, then H moves to G. Hence if a line meets a cubic in A, D, G, the tangents there cut the cubic again in collinear points.

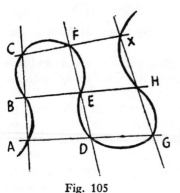

Fig. 105

(5) If B and E are flexes, and both A and C move to B, and D and F move to E, then X and G move to H. Hence the *line which joins two flexes of a cubic goes through a third flex.*

168. *Class and Order.* The "*class*" of a curve is the number of tangents which can be drawn to it from a general point. We want to find an expression for it.

If $f(x, y, z) = 0$ is the equation of the curve, the tangent at (x', y', z') has the equation $xf_{x'} + yf_{y'} + zf_{z'} = 0$, where $f_{x'}$, $f_{y'}$, $f_{z'}$ denote the partial derivatives of f for x, y, z

---

* A "*reducible*" curve is one which splits into curves of lower degree. Usually we assume our curves to be irreducible. A "*non-singular*" curve is one without singular points,

respectively at x', y', z'. For instance, the tangent at (x', y', z') to

$$x^3 + y^3 + z^3 - 3kxyz = 0 \qquad (1)$$

is $\quad x(x'^2 - ky'z') + y(y'^2 - kz'x') + z(z'^2 - kx'y') = 0.$

The tangent goes through the point (a, b, c) if

$$af_{x'} + bf_{y'} + cf_{z'} = 0.$$

The curve $\qquad\qquad af_x + bf_y + cf_z = 0$

is called the "polar" of (a, b, c) for the curve.

Thus the polar of (a, b, c) for our cubic (1), is

$$a(x^2 - kyz) + b(y^2 - kzx) + c(z^2 - kxy) = 0.$$

This is usually called the first polar, but we do not consider other polars.

Obviously the polar goes through all points of contact of tangents from (a, b, c) to the curve, and as it is of degree $n - 1$, it meets f in $n(n - 1)$ points, and it would appear that the class ν of f is $n(n - 1)$.

Dually for a curve of class ν, the number of points where it meets a general line would appear to be $\nu(\nu - 1)$.

But this obviously leads to a contradiction: a cubic $(n = 3)$, would have class 6, and the order of a curve of class 6 would be 30 and not 3.

The error arises because, in considering the number of the cuts of two curves, we neglected their singular points. This difficulty must be faced.

169. *Hessian.* Before doing so, we consider some cases of polar curves. The polar of a point for a conic, as defined here, coincides with the earlier definition in Chap. III. If f be a cubic, the polar of (a, b, c) is the conic

$$aU + bV + cW \doteq 0, \qquad (1)$$

where U, V, W stand for $\delta f/\delta x$, $\delta f/\delta y$, $\delta f/\delta z$, and $U = 0$, $V = 0$, $W = 0$ represent conics.

If we vary the point (a, b, c) we get a "net" of conics. Some of these will be line-pairs. Using the work on p. 49, we find that (1) is a line-pair if the following equations can hold simultaneously:

$$\begin{aligned}
aU_x + bV_x + cW_x &= 0, \\
aU_y + bV_y + cW_y &= 0, \\
aU_z + bV_z + cW_z &= 0,
\end{aligned} \qquad (2)$$

where U_x stands for $\delta U/\delta x$, and so on (the left-hand sides of (2) correspond to X, Y, Z on p. 49).

Since a, b, c do not all vanish, these equations can only hold when the determinant of the coefficients of a, b, c is zero, and since each coefficient U_r, V_x, ... is linear in x, y, z, the determinant is a *cubic* in x, y, z.

Also when the determinant vanishes, the common point (or double-point), of the line-pair satisfies each of equations (2). Hence the locus of the double points of degenerate polar conics of a cubic is a cubic.

For a general n-ic, since $U = \delta f/\delta x$, the determinant is

$$\begin{vmatrix} f_{xx}, & f_{xy}, & f_{xz} \\ f_{xy}, & f_{yy}, & f_{yz} \\ f_{xz}, & f_{yz}, & f_{zz} \end{vmatrix} = 0$$

where $f_{xx} = \delta^2 f/\delta x^2$, $f_{xy} = \delta^2 f/\delta x \delta y$, ... and so on.

The determinant is the *"Hessian"* of f, and has degree $3(n-2)$.

Reverting to the cubic, it can be shewn that, if the polar conic of P has a double point at Q, and thus Q is on the Hessian, then the polar conic of Q has a double point at P, which is thus also on the Hessian, and it is natural to call P, Q *"conjugate"* points on the Hessian.

Dually, a *"class-cubic"*, or *"cubic* envelope", that is, a curve of class three, has a conic envelope corresponding to each line of the plane. This degenerates to a point-pair, when the line touches a certain other class-cubic, and then the join of the point-pair touches the same class-cubic.

170. *Plücker's Equations*. We shall at first assume our loci have no singularities except nodes and cusps. For a general n-ic f, we find by calculation that, if f has a node, the polar of a point P, not on a tangent at the node, goes through the node, and that, as we might expect, the node counts as two of the cuts of f and the polar of P. If f has a cusp, and P is not on the tangent there, the polar of P touches that tangent at the cusp, and the cusp must be counted as three cuts. The justification for these and other numbers is given later. Meanwhile we note that a curve has an equation of form

$y^2 = hx^3 + \ldots$ near a cusp, if the cusp is taken as origin, and the tangent there as the x-axis; while the polar of P has an equation of form $y = kx^2 + \ldots$ near the cusp.

Thus if f has δ nodes and $\varkappa$ cusps, these absorb $2\delta + 3\varkappa$ of the cuts of f with the polar of a general point P. The other cuts are at the points of contact of tangents to f from P. Hence the class ν of f is

$$\nu = n(n - 1) - 2\delta - 3\varkappa.$$

Thus a cubic without a node or cusp has class six; this is reduced to four or three when the cubic has a node or cusp respectively.

The Hessian of f goes through each flex of f just once; it goes through each node of f and has a node there, the tangents to the Hessian and the curve at the node are the same; it goes through each cusp, but there it has a triple point, two of whose tangents coincide with the cuspidal tangent. In general it has no other singularities. The number of cuts of f and its Hessian is six for each node, eight for each cusp, and as the order of the Hessian is $3(n - 2)$, we get for the number ι of flexes:

$$\iota = 3n(n - 2) - 6\delta - 8\varkappa.$$

The other Plücker equations are duals of those given. If τ be the number of bitangents, then

$$n = \nu(\nu - 1) - 2\tau - 3\iota, \quad \varkappa = 3\nu(\nu - 2) - 6\tau - 8\iota.$$

Hence $\iota - \varkappa = 3(\nu - n)$, $\tau - \delta = \frac{1}{2}(\nu - n)(\nu + n - 9)$.

A non-singular locus has $\delta = \varkappa = 0$, a non-singular envelope has $\tau = \iota = 0$. Thus every curve is singular, either as locus, or as envelope, or as both. This removes the difficulty mentioned in § 168.

In particular for a non-singular quartic locus ($n = 4$, $\nu = 12$, $\delta = \kappa = 0$), we have $\tau = 28$. See Fig. 25.

All singularities, real and imaginary, are counted in Plücker's equations. To get a relation for *real* singularities, arguments of a totally different nature are needed, and these lead to the only other independent relation, that of Klein:

$$n + 2\tau' + \iota' = \nu + 2\delta' + \varkappa',$$

where δ' is the number of real isolated points, $\varkappa'$ that of real cusps, ι' of real flexes, τ' of real bitangents with imaginary points of contact. A bitangent of this kind is dual to an isolated point, which is real, but has imaginary tangents at it.

171. *Flexes of a cubic locus.* Plücker's equations shew that a *non-singular* cubic locus ($\delta = \varkappa = 0$) has nine flexes, real or imaginary, and Klein's equation shews that if the equation of a non-singular cubic be real, it has just three real flexes. We saw that the join of two flexes (real or imaginary), goes through a third flex. It follows that the nine flexes must be arranged like the points A, B, C, A', B', C', L, M, N in the figure of Pappus' theorem (Fig. 43), with the addition that the triads ALA', BMB', CNC' are also collinear.

As a flex F is on the Hessian, its polar conic is a line-pair; it is in fact the tangent at F, together with the "*harmonic polar*" of F, which joins the (collinear) points of contact of the *three* tangents from F to the cubic (see below).

The join of two flexes, and the harmonic polars of the flexes, form a very convenient triangle of reference for the cubic which then acquires the equation

$$x^3 + y^3 + z^3 + 6m\ xyz = 0. \tag{1}$$

The Hessian is then given by the same equation with m replaced by μ, where

$$\mu = -(1 + 2m^3)/6m^2.$$

Hence there are three cubics which have a given Hessian.

The equation (1) illustrates another important fact; whereas all conics are projectively equivalent, not all non-singular cubics are so; for m is connected with a projective invariant, namely the cross-ratio of the *four* tangents which can be drawn to a cubic from a point on it; this cross-ratio is independent of the point chosen, and it must be the same for two projectively equivalent cubics. We note that as a non-singular cubic is of class six, six tangents go to it from an arbitrary point. If the point is on the cubic, two of these are absorbed at the tangent there, three if the point is a flex.

172. *Cubic envelope.* We illustrated in Chap. II the main forms of cubic loci. A cubic envelope, or class-cubic, is the envelope of a line whose co-ordinates (l, m, n) satisfy a homogeneous cubic equation.

The maximum number of cusps for a quartic locus is three;

its class is then three; it is a cubic envelope. The cusps are dual to three collinear flexes on a cubic locus, and hence their cuspidal tangents concur.

An example is given by

$$\frac{1}{\sqrt{x}} + \frac{1}{\sqrt{y}} + \frac{1}{\sqrt{z}} = 0; \qquad (1)$$

here the cusps are at the vertices of the triangle of reference. It is the hypocycloid given in Fig. 29, when the triangle is equliateral.

If we write ξ, γ, ζ for x, y, z in (1), and make the transformation $\xi = x + iy$, $\gamma = x - iy$, $\zeta = \frac{1}{2}az$ (which is tantamount to taking OIJ as the above reference triangle, if x, y, z be homogeneous Cartesian co-ordinates), the equation becomes (if $z = 1$),

$$(x^2 + y^2 - ax)^2 - a^2(x^2 + y^2) = 0,$$

or, in polars, $r = a(1 + \cos \theta)$, a cardioid (Fig. 26).

Hence a cardioid has cusps at I, J. The hypocycloid has the line at infinity as a bitangent, touching that curve at I, J.

Another type of a cubic envelope is shaped like (1), together with an oval curve surrounding that curve.

173. *An application to conics.* We could begin with three conics U, V, W, not in a pencil, and consider the "*net*" of conics $k_1U + k_2V + k_3W = 0$, any conic in the net being given by the ratios $k_1 : k_2 : k_3$. If the point P be such that its polars for U, V, W concur in Q, say, its polars for all conics of the net go through Q. The locus of such points P is a cubic locus, the "*Jacobian*" of the net, and Q is on it. If PQ cuts this cubic again in R, the line PQ and a certain line through R together form a degenerate conic of the net. The cubic can be regarded as the Hessian of another (§171); the net of conics is then the net of polar conics of the latter cubic.

Now PQ envelopes a cubic envelope which also arises, dually, as follows: There is a net of conic envelopes $k_1\Sigma_1 + k_2\Sigma_2 + k_3\Sigma_3 = 0$, each of which is apolar to each conic of the first net (§ 59). If the line l is such that its poles for $\Sigma_1, \Sigma_2, \Sigma_3$ lie on a line m, say, then the poles of l for all conics of the Σ-net lie on m, and the same cubic envelope is described by l, by m, and by PQ. This Σ-net contains degenerate point-pair conics, one of which is the pair P, Q and another consists of the cut lm and another point.

A special case is of most interest. Suppose Σ_3 is the pair I, $\mathcal{J}$. Then $k_1\Sigma_1 + k_2\Sigma_2$ is a pencil of conic envelopes touching four lines, and the Σ-net consists of all conics confocal to any of them. The degenerate point-pair envelopes are I, $\mathcal{J}$ and the pairs of foci. Hence the locus of the foci of conics touching four lines is a cubic through I, $\mathcal{J}$. The envelope of the principal axes of the conics is a cubic envelope touching the line at infinity. The conic loci apolar to our conic envelopes have I, $\mathcal{J}$ as conjugate points, and hence are rectangular hyperbolas (§ 56). The degenerate conics of this net are their asymptotes.

Suppose, in particular, one of the common tangents to Σ_1, Σ_2 is the line at infinity; the cubic envelope then touches that line at I, $\mathcal{J}$, and is a tricusped-hypocycloid (§ 172). Hence the envelope of the axes of parabolas touching three lines is such a curve; so is the envelope of Simson lines of points on the circumcircle of the three lines; and so is the envelope of the asymptotes of rectangular hyperbolas which go through four orthocentric points.

174. *Genus.* An (irreducible) n-ic cannot have more than $N = \frac{1}{2}(n-1)(n-2)$ nodes and cusps. For suppose it had $N + 1$. Then through them and $\frac{1}{2}(n+2)(n-1) - (N+1)$ other points we can draw an $(n-1)$-ic. This cuts the n-ic in $\frac{1}{2}(n+2)(n-1) + N + 1$ points, counting two at each node and cusp. But this number is $n(n-1) + 1$, whereas an n-ic and an $n-1$-ic can cut only in $n(n-1)$ points. It can be shewn that the number N can be attained.

The *"genus"* of an n-ic is defined as
$$p = \tfrac{1}{2}(n-1)(n-2) - \delta - \varkappa.$$
It is the number of nodes and cusps it might have, but hasn't.

175. *Quadratic transformation.* The properties so far investigated have been invariant under projection; for example, a polar curve or a Hessian of a curve project into such curves.

We take a step of great significance when we consider the quadratic transformation
$$x' = 1/x, \; y' = 1/y, \; z' = 1/z,$$

which by § 58, turns a line into a conic round the reference triangle.

A conic which touches the sides of the triangle has an equation

$(ax)^{\frac{1}{2}} + (by)^{\frac{1}{2}} + (cz)^{\frac{1}{2}} = 0,$

which by the transformation becomes

$(a/x)^{\frac{1}{2}} + (b/y)^{\frac{1}{2}} + (d/z)^{\frac{1}{2}} = 0.$

This is a projection of the tricusped-hypocycloid of § 172. A conic which cuts a

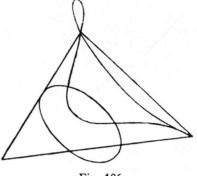

Fig. 106

side becomes a quartic with a node or an isolated point at the opposite vertex, according as the cuts are real or imaginary.

The dual quadratic transformation (§ 58), turns a conic envelope into a curve of class four. In particular an ellipse and the locus of its centres of curvature (§ 35), are so related as envelopes.

What is of most importance is the following; we omit the proof: *The quadratic transformation does not change the genus of a curve.*

Suppose $p = 0$. The curve has then the maximum number of nodes and cusps possible for its degree. It can then be proved that there are polynomials f_i in a parameter t such that

$$x : y : z = f_1(t) : f_2(t) : f_3(t), \qquad (1)$$

and further, that these can be chosen so that to each point of the curve (except perhaps for a finite set), corresponds just one t. Such a curve is called *"unicursal"*, not a happy name, for it may have an isolated point.

Thus a cubic with a node or cusp, and a quartic with three cusps, are unicursal. So is the astroid (Fig. 28), for besides the four visible cusps, it has one at each of I, $\mathcal{J}$, and has imaginary nodes at $(\pm ia, \pm ia)$, where $OA = a$. These reduce its class to $30 - 2.4 - 3.6 = 4$. Its equation can be put in the form, if $a = 1$,

$$x : y : z = (t^2 - 1)^3 : (2t)^3 : (t^2 + 1)^3.$$

A curve expressed in form (1), where f are any one-valued functions, is said to be *"uniformized"*. Unicursal curves are

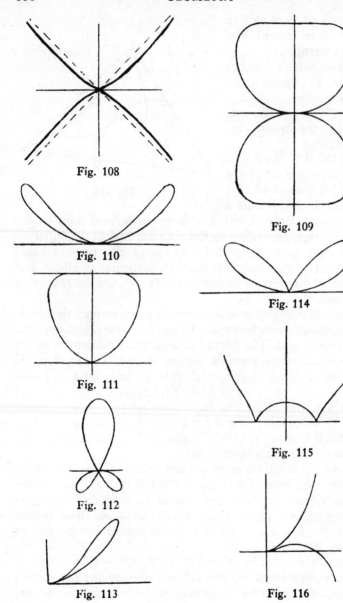

Fig. 108

Fig. 109

Fig. 110

Fig. 114

Fig. 111

Fig. 115

Fig. 112

Fig. 113

Fig. 116

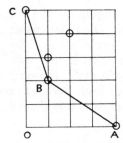

Fig. 107

hence uniformized by polynomials; but general algebraic curves need automorphic functions and the theory is difficult and extensive.

176. *Expansions at the origin.* So far we have ignored all singularities of loci except nodes and cusps. For more complicated ones we use a method which goes back to Newton.

Consider, for example,

$$x^4 + ax^2y^4 + bxy^3 - xy^2 + y^5 = 0.$$

Plot the *terms* of this expression on squared paper, representing $x^r y^s$ (ignoring its coefficient), by the point $x = r$, $y = s$. Throw a string round the points to cordon them off from the origin. The string catches at points A, B, C representing x^4, xy^2, y^5. Take the terms on the straight portions of the string, and discard any factors that are powers of x and y. We get

$$x^3 = y^2, \quad y^3 = x.$$

Then these give the branches at the origin: that point is a combination of a cusp and a flex. The expansions of y at the origin in terms of x begin with

$$y = x^{\frac{1}{3}}, \quad y = \pm x^{\frac{3}{2}}$$

These are the real branches, but there are also imaginary branches, begining with

$$y = \omega x^{\frac{1}{3}}, \quad y = \omega^2 x^{\frac{1}{3}}, \text{ where } \omega^3 = 1, \omega \neq 1.$$

Generally, if $f(x, y) = 0$ goes through the origin, the branches there are arranged in sets of cycles, of which a typical set is the r branches of form

$$y = ax^{s/r} + a_1 x^{(s+1)/r} + \ldots,$$
$$y = \theta a x^{s/r} + a_2 x^{(s+1)/r} + \ldots,$$
$$y = \theta^2 a x^{s/r} + a_3 x^{(s+1)/r} + \ldots,$$

and so on, where $\theta^r = 1$. If r is odd, only one of these is real; if r is even, two.

We call r the "order" of the cycle, it is the number of points in which a general line through O, or through a point near O, cuts the branches.

The *"order"* or "multiplicity" of the singularity at O is the number of branches that go through O, (The name "branch" is often used for what we call a "cycle").

177. *Illustrations from quartics.* If the quartic has two distinct branches (real or not), not in a cycle at O, the only case which calls for comment is when one or both have a flex at O. The latter is the case for the lemniscate, which is shaped like a figure-of-eight, and the curious curve

$$x^4 - y^4 + x^2 - 2y^2 = 0$$

which is made up of two odd branches, that is, each is cut by a line in an odd number of points. (Fig. 108.)

Fig. 109. $y^2 = x^4 + y^4$ shews a *"tacnode"*: the approximation at (0, 0) is $y = \pm (x^2 + \frac{1}{2}x^6 +)$.

Fig. 110. $(y - x^2)^2 = y^2(x^2 - y^2)$; *"oscnode"*; approximation $y = x^2 \pm x^3$.

Fig. 111. $y^3 = x^4 + y^4$. There is a triple point at (0, 0), two branches being imaginary.

Fig. 112. $y(y^2 - x^2) = x^4 + y^4$. Triple point with real branches in distinct cycles, $y = x + \ldots$, $y = -x + \ldots$, $y = -x^2 + \ldots$, one in each cycle.

Fig. 113. $(y - x^2)^2 = xy^3 - y^4$; "oscnode-cusp"; approximation $y = x^2 \pm x^{\frac{7}{2}}$.

Fig. 114. $yx^2 = x^4 + y^4$; triple point: approximation $y = x^2, y^3 = x^2$.

Fig. 115. $(x^2 - 1)^2 = y^3$. Two cusps.

Fig. 116. Illustrates the important case of the *"beak"*. Near the origin $y = ax^2 \pm bx^{\frac{5}{2}} = ax^{\frac{1}{2}} \pm bx^{\frac{1}{2}}$. This is the case for the curve $(y - x^2)^2 = xy^2 + x^3y$. The beak is a type of cuspidal branch which must be distinguished from the simple cusp, where $y = ax^{\frac{3}{2}} + \ldots$.

178. *Number of intersections.* We can now say a little on the question, so long postponed, of the number of cuts to be counted when curves meet in singular points. It might be expected, and is fortunately true, that this is the sum of the numbers to be counted for each pair of cycles. In the simplest case when the two cycles have no common tangent at P, the number of cuts is the product of their orders.

But the general case is very complicated, and we have space for only a few instances.

If a branch of one curve is of form
$$y = a_1 x + a_2 x^2 + \ldots\ldots + a_{t-1} x^{t-1} + a_t x^t,$$
and a branch of another has the same form with the same $a_1, a_2, \ldots, a_{t-1}$ but different a_t, the number of cuts is t. Branches of this land are called *"linear"*.

A linear branch and an "ordinary" cusp, i.e. one where the equation is $y = ax^{(v+1)/v} + \ldots$, have v or $v+1$ cuts according as the tangents are distinct, or not. Two cuspidal cycles of orders v, μ have $v\mu$ cuts, if the tangents are distinct; if $v > \mu$ and the first cusp is ordinary, the number is $(v+1)\mu$ in case of tangency.

179. *Reduction of singularities.* We now indicate how, by a series of quadratic transformations, we can reduce the singularities of a curve to *"ordinary"* ones, i.e. to multiple points with *distinct* tangents. The clue is that a vertex of a fundamental triangle corresponds to all points of the opposite side, but distinct directions at the vertex correspond to distinct points of the side, when we perform a quadratic transformation.

Suppose A is a point of multiplicity r, and of any complexity on an irreducible curve of order n. Take A as a vertex of a fundamental triangle ABC, with B, C not on the curve, and such that AB, AC meet the curve in $n-r$ distinct points, apart from A. The quadratic transformation, of which ABC is the fundamental triangle, turns our curve into one of order $2n - r$ with singularities of orders n, $n - r$, $n - r$ respectively at A, B, C. But these singularities are now ordinary. If other singularities appear at points of BC, the sum of their orders is not greater than r. Finally we can replace each non-ordinary singularity by a set of ordinary singularities.

If now we reconsider Plücker's equations, we shall find we can retain them for all sorts of singularities, if we regard any singularity as a combination of nodes and cusps: for example an ordinary n-fold point as $\frac{1}{2}n(n-1)$ nodes, a beak as a *node and cusp*, in their effect on the class of the curve.

This kind of equivalence enables us to extend the definition of genus to algebraic curves with any kind of singularities and so that a quadratic transformation leaves it unchanged.

180. *Noether's Fundamental Theorem.* The following is an obvious generalization of the projective definition of conics. If φ, ψ be curves of order n and φ_1, ψ_1 curves of order n_1 the locus of the cuts of curves $\varphi + k\psi = 0$ and $\varphi_1 + k\psi_1 = 0$, with the same k, as k varies, is $\varphi\psi_1 - \varphi_1\psi = 0$, in general a curve of order $n + n_1$, and this goes through all the cuts of φ, ψ and all the cuts of φ_1, ψ_1. We call the two pencils $\varphi + k\psi = 0$ and $\varphi_1 + k\psi_1 = 0$ *"projective"*.

Thus from a pencil of lines and a projective pencil of conics we get a cubic; from two projective pencils of conics, we get a quartic; and, in fact, any cubic and any quartic can be so generated.

First, a remark on pencils of curves: if a point is assigned as an ordinary r-fold point, this is tantamount to imposing $\frac{1}{2}r(r + 1)$ conditions, but if the point is not ordinary, so that some tangents have to coincide, this imposes extra conditions. Thus a given cusp, tacnode, beak impose respectively 4, 5, 6 conditions; and if the curve is not of too low an order, these conditions are independent.

We now ask, what is the general equation of the curve which goes through all the cuts of curves f, φ, of any orders? Difficulties arise when these cuts are singularities of one or both curves. The general theorem is Noether's, and we state it for ordinary singularities:

If a curve has a singularity of order $r + s - 1$, or more, at all cuts where f, φ have singularities of any orders r, s, respectively then the curve is of form $f\varphi_1 + \varphi f_1 = 0$, where f_1, φ_1 have singularities of orders $r - 1$, $s - 1$ at least at the points.*

In particular, if an n-ic and an $n_1 + n_2$-ic meet at all the cuts of the n-ic and an n_1-ic, their remaining points of meeting are at all the cuts of the n-ic and an n_2-ic. This gives us, for example: if through the six points where a cubic C_1 and a conic S meet, another cubic C_2 drawn, then the other three cuts of C_1, C_2 are collinear. Compare this with § 167 (2) (3).

* If the order of the singularity is one, the point is non-singular.

181. *Residual sets of points*. A curve which has a singularity of order at least $r - 1$ wherever f has one of order r is called an "*adjoint*" to f. If two sets of points G_1, G_2 together constitute all the non-singular cuts of f by some adjoint to f, they are called "*residual sets*" on f.

Then if G_1 be also residual to G'_2, and G_2 to G'_1, then G'_1 is residual to G'_2. For G_1, G_2 are cut out by φ, say; G_1, G'_2 by φ_1, G_2, G'_1 by φ_2, where φ, φ_1, φ_2 are adjoints to f. As $\varphi_1\varphi_2$ contains G_1 and G_2, and, wherever f has multiplicity r, it has multiplicity $2(r - 1) = r + (r - 1) - 1$, or more, we have by Noether's theorem

$$\varphi_1\varphi_2 = \theta f + \theta_1\varphi$$

where $\theta_1 = 0$ is an adjoint curve of f which contains G'_1, G'_2.

The meaning of this important theorem is best grasped in a simpler case. The statement is still true when G_1, G_2 are sets of ordinary points which together form the total intersection of f with some curve φ; and similarly for G'_1, G'_2. It can then be stated as an extension of the six-circles theorem, the letters A, B, now denoting *sets* of ordinary points on curves: If three curves C_k, C_l, C_n (the subscripts denoting orders) meet in the set A', and meet again in pairs, namely C_k, C_l in B; C_k, C_n in C; C_l, C_n in D'; then we can find curves C_k', C_l', C_n', in many ways, with $k + k' = l + l' = n + n'$, through D'. C, B respectively, such that C_n' and C_l' meet C_k in the same set D, and C_l', C_k' meet C_n in the same set B', and C', C_n' meet C_l in the same set C', and all three C_k', C_l', C_n' meet in the same set A.

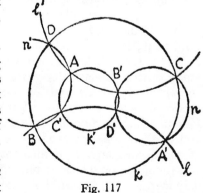

181. *Cremona Transformations*. The most interesting properties of algebraic curves are those which are invariant not merely for collineations but for the wider set of "*birational*" transformations. These are of two kinds. In the first, the "*Cremona transformations*", each point

Fig. 117

$P(x, y, z)$ of a plane is transformed into a point $P'(x', y', z')$, where x', y', z' are polynomials, homogeneous and of the same degree in x, y, z, so chosen that x, y, z are also polynomials, homogeneous and of the same degree in x', y', z', and so that the correspondence between P and P' is one-to-one, except that a finite number of points may correspond each to all points of a curve. The simplest case is the quadratic transformation, and by a magnificent theorem of Noether's: every Cremona transformation is the product of quadratic transformations and collineations.

Hence these transformations do not change the genus of a curve, but this property is shared by the other type of birational transformations. These are restricted to points of two curves, the co-ordinates of each point of one being homogeneous polynomials, of the same degree, in the co-ordinates of a point of the other; what happens in the rest of the plane does not matter.

We have seen that, by a sequence of quadratic transformations, an irreducible curve can be turned into one with only ordinary singularities; if we use the wider type of birational transformations, it can be turned into one with no singularities except, perhaps, nodes, and if we do not mind leaving the plane, it can be turned into a curve in ordinary space with no singularities at all.

Thus any curve of genus *one* can be birationally transformed into a non-singular plane cubic.

182. Further development of the theory of plane curves is only fruitful when it is connected with the theory of Riemann surfaces and Abelian functions. This has been a favourite study during the last fifty years, of the Italian geometers, and they have also made contributions of great beauty to a similar theory of surfaces and of "Varieties" of higher dimensions. Herein a combination of the theory of integrals on the varieties, and of their topology, yields the decisive results. The theory of curves and surfaces is thus connected with modern algebra and topology, on which so much work is done to-day. We can only mention the existence of this extensive and elegant theory.

CHAPTER X

MANY DIMENSIONS AND REPRESENTATIONAL GEOMETRY

183. *Dependent points.* In three-dimensional space we used four homogeneous co-ordinates, real or complex, referred to a tetrahedron of reference. The co-ordinates of the vertices of the tetrahedron were $(1, 0, 0, 0)$, $(0, 1, 0, 0)$, $(0, 0, 1, 0)$ and $(0, 0, 0, 1)$.

We generalize this algebraically to space of $n - 1$ dimensions. A set of n numbers $(x_1, x_2, \ldots x_n)$ not all zero, will be called a "*point*", and may be denoted by x. Only the ratios are relevant, so that $(kx_1, \ldots, kx_n)$ will be the same point for all non-zero k. The points $(1, 0, \ldots 0)$, $(0, 1, 0, \ldots 0)$, $(0, 0, 1, 0, \ldots 0)$, $\ldots (0, 0, \ldots 0, 1)$ are "*reference points*".

If $(p_1, \ldots, p_n)$, $(q_1, \ldots, q_n)$, $\ldots$ be points p, q, $\ldots$, we shall write
$$k_1 p + k_2 q + \ldots\ldots = 0 \ (k_1, k_2, \ldots \text{ constants}),$$
to stand for the n equations
$$k_1 p_i + k_2 q_i + \ldots\ldots = 0 \ (i = 1 \ldots\ldots n).$$
If such equations, with the k_1, k_2, k_3, $\ldots$ not all zero, can be found for p, q, r, we say these three points "*lie on a line*"; if for p, q, r, s, we say they "*lie on a plane*", and so on for spaces of 3, 4 $\ldots$ dimensions. Such sets of points are called "*dependent*" sets. The n reference points are independent.

Just as, in three dimensions, we could take any tetrahedron as the tetrahedron of reference, so here, we can take any n independent points as reference points. Then $(x_1, \ldots, x_n)$ and $(y_1, \ldots, y_n)$ will be the same point, referred respectively to the old and the new reference figure, if
$$y_i = \Sigma a_{ij} x_j \tag{1}$$
for some constants, a_{ij}, where, as always, the summation is from 1 to n, for each repeated suffix, in this case j.

We write det a_{ij} for the determinant of the a_{ij}.

We could also regard (1) as a transformation, with a *fixed* reference figure, which turns the point x into the point y (Cf. § 40). This transformation is a *"collineation"*, turning collinear, coplanar, ... sets of points into such sets. It has, in general, just n self-corresponding points.

So far we have treated the matter algebraically. We could also construct an abstract geometry as in Chapters IV, VI, and then introduce co-ordinates. Then we should call $(x_1, \ldots, x_n)$ the "co-ordinates" of the point x. It is best to keep the algebraical and the geometrical views simultaneously in mind, as in the case of lower dimensions.

A subspace of $n - 2$ dimensions, in space of $n - 1$ dimensions, will be called a *"prime"*, following Baker. It corresponds to a plane in three-dimensional geometry; its points satisfy a linear equation $\Sigma \pi_i x_i = 0$, and $(\pi_1, \pi_2, \ldots, \pi_n)$ are the *"homogeneous co-ordinates"* of the prime π.

It can be shewn, either by an algebraical or by a geometric argument, that in *four* dimensions ($n = 5$), if a, b, c, d, e be independent points, then the plane abc and the line de do not meet, and that if a, b, c, d, f be also independent, then the planes abc, def meet in just one point; further, three lines have, in general, just one transversal line, and, in general, a single infinity of planes can be drawn through a given point to meet three lines.

184. *Quadrics, polarities, null-systems.* Some notions of solid geometry transfer at once to $n - 1$ dimensions. Thus, corresponding to a quadric, we have a curved figure of $n - 2$ dimensions with equation

$$\Sigma a_{ij} x_i x_j = 0, \ (a_{ij} = a_{ji})$$

using the summation rule above. This *"quadric"* is *"non-singular"* (i.e. does not resemble a cone, or plane-pair), if det $a_{ij} \neq 0$.

Two points x, y are *"conjugate"* for the quadric, if

$$\Sigma a_{ij} x_i y_j = 0,$$

and then y lies on the prime with co-ordinates

$$\pi_j = \Sigma x_i a_{ij}, \tag{1}$$

the *"polar prime"* of x.

But if $a_{ij} = -a_{ji}$ $(i, j = 1 \dots n)$, the points x and primes π connected by (1), resemble a null-system in three dimensions; each point lies on its corresponding prime. But if n is odd, det $a_{ij} = 0$, since a skew determinant of odd order vanishes. Hence it is only for odd dimensions (n even), that we have a genuine analogue.

A quadric can, by suitable choice of reference figure, always be brought to the form $\Sigma k_i x_i{}^2 = 0$; the reference figure is then "*self-polar*" for the quadric. If the quadric is non-singular, no k_i vanishes. For *real* co-ordinates, a quadric with an equation with real coefficients can be reduced to this form with all k_i real, and then, in this case if r of the k_i be positive and $n - r$ negative, and we arrange that $r \geq n - r$, as we obviously can, the equation cannot be transformed to one with a different value of r by any change of reference figure.

It is because of this "*law of inertia*" that we can distinguish in ordinary space between ellipsoids and the two types of hyperboloids, a distinction which disappears when we use complex co-ordinates.

185. *Representational Geometry.* We propose first to connect the projective geometry on a *line* (with complex co-ordinates), and the geometry of *space*.

The points on the line can be put into correspondence with those of a Euclidean (or inversion), plane by means of the Argand diagram, if we make the point $z = x + iy$ of the line correspond to the point (x, y) of the plane.

On the projective line any projective transformation is of form

$$z' = \frac{az + b}{cz + d}, \quad ad - bc \neq 0, \quad a, b, c, d \text{ complex.} \quad (1)$$

This leaves unchanged the cross-ratio of four points z_1, z_2, z_3, z_4, defined as

$$(z_1 - z_2)(z_3 - z_4)/(z_2 - z_3)(z_4 - z_1) \quad (2)$$

The transformation is fixed by the fate of three points, and is the product of two involutions (§ 84).

On the Argand diagram (§ 27), the transformation (1) is a *circular transformation* i.e. it turns a circle into a circle, if we regard the line as a special kind of circle. Indeed the invariant (2) is real if, and only if, the four points lie on a circle (or line).

The transformation is the product of two "*Möbius involutions*" defined as follows, in a plane.

Let X, Y be fixed points, then by a Möbius involution, P becomes P' on the circle PXY and P, P' separate X, Y harmonically on the circle. This involution is the product of inversions in two orthogonal circles through X, Y, whereof either the first or the second may be any circle through X, Y.

Now invert the plane into a sphere; circles on the plane become circles on the sphere; circular transformations become circular transformations; and each is fixed by the fate of three points, as is now obvious; each is the product of two involutions, where an involution is defined as follows: if X, Y be fixed points on the sphere, the transform of P (on the sphere), is that point P' on the sphere such that the line PP' meets both XY and the polar line of XY for the sphere. We say P, P' separate X, Y harmonically on the sphere.

This suggests that we now regard our sphere as immersed in Euclidean space, made projective. Instead of a circle on a sphere, we then think of the plane which cuts the sphere in that circle. The circular transformations turn planes into planes, and leave the sphere invariant.

The involution on the sphere can now be extended to all space: if XY, $X'Y'$ are polar lines for the sphere, then P becomes P', if PP' cuts these lines in points which separate P, P' harmonically. The same definition applies to any quadric; we have a "*biaxial involution*", and (§ 140) any collineation which leaves a quadric invariant is the product of two such involutions, if it is direct, i.e. does not interchange the reguli on the quadric.

If we take the sphere (or quadric) as the absolute quadric in a model of non-Euclidean geometry of three dimensions (Cf. § 108), a displacement corresponds to a direct collineation leaving this quadric invariant; it is hence a product of two reflections in lines, for these correspond to biaxial involutions, since a line "perpendicular" to a line l meets l and the polar line of l for the absolute (Cf. § 109a).

If on the sphere X_1, X_2 separate A_1, A_2 harmonically, then X_1X_2 cuts A_1A_2 and the polar line of A_1A_2. Now on a projective line (or conic), if A_1A_2, B_1B_2, C_1C_2 be point-pairs, and $A'_1A'_2$ separate B_1B_2, C_1C_2 harmonically, with similar meanings for $B'_1B'_2$, $C'_1C'_2$, then $A'_1 A'_2$, $B'_1 B'_2$, $C'_1 C'_2$ have a common harmonic separator.

On the conic this is virtually *Hesse's theorem*: if $B'C'$, $C'A'$, $A'B'$ be the polars of A, B, C respectively, then AA', BB', CC' meet.

The corresponding theorem on the sphere, when we treat it as the absolute quadric, gives the *Morley-Petersen* theorem: if l, m, n be skew lines in hyperbolic space, and l' the common perpendicular of m, n and similarly for m', n', then l', m', n' have a common perpendicular. This is also true in Euclidean space.

186. *Oriented Circles*. In the above, instead of replacing a circle on a sphere by the plane in which it lies, we could replace it by the pole of that plane. Circles on the sphere are then represented by points outside the sphere, orthogonal circles by conjugate points.

This suggests that we try to represent circles in a plane by points of space: the simplest way is to represent a circle by the point vertically above its centre (the plane being horizontal), at a height equal to the radius of the circle. This would use only the upper half of space, but if we give the circles an orientation, or sense of turning, we can let points above the plane represent the circles with a right-hand turn, and those below, circles with a left-hand turn. The first can be regarded as having positive radii; the second, negative radii. Thus each circle, in the usual sense, now enters twice, once with each orientation. The points on the plane itself, represent point-circles.

At the same time we must orient our lines, by giving them directions, and in the rest of this section, *by "circle" and "line" we mean the oriented figures*, unless the contrary is stated.

Two circles *"touch"* when they have a common point, *and* a common direction of turn at the point; they fit like cogged wheels in motion. Similarly for a line "touching" a circle.

Thus two circles with centres (x, y), (x', y') and radii r, r' (positive or negative), touch if, and only if

$$(x - x')^2 + (y - y')^2 = (r - r')^2.$$

Two circles mutually external have just *one* common pair of tangents; any two circles have just *one* centre of similitude.

To get the space representation of a line, we regard it as the envelope of the tangent circles; these circles are represented by points on a plane through the line, at 45° to the base-plane. We take this inclined plane to represent the line. The other plane through the line at 45° to the base-plane represents the line with the opposite orientation.

All these inclined planes touch the same real circle at infinity.

Let us compare inversion geometry with the present geometry. In the former, we have systems of coaxal (non-oriented) circles; circles in the same system have, in pairs, the same radical axis, and they meet in two fixed points, real or not. Here we have systems of oriented circles; circles in the same system have, in pairs, the same centre of similitude, and they all touch two fixed lines, real or not. Three given circles, not in the same system, fix three centres of similitude, and these lie on the "axis of similitude" of the three; this corresponds to the radical centre in inversion geometry.

The transformations in the plane which turn lines into lines, circles into circles, and preserve tangency form a group, the "*Laguerre group*". They turn a set of circles, triads of which have the same axis of similitude, into such a set: Points may become circles, and vice versa, by these transformations. The corresponding transformations in the space representation, are collineations which leave invariant the circle at infinity mentioned above. They form a group which resembles the group of direct and indirect displacements and similitudes of Euclidean space, since the latter group leaves an imaginary circle at infinity invariant. The subgroup which resembles the group of displacements leaves invariant the square of the tangential interval between two circles, or more generally, $d^2 - (r_1 - r_2)^2$, where r_1, r_2 are the radii, positive or negative, of the circles, and d is the distance between their centres.

If we wish for the analogue of direct displacements, we must preserve orientations when we transform.

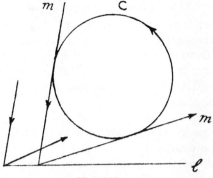

Fig. 117a

The transformation in this geometry, which corresponds to inversion in inversion geometry, is rather a surprise. Take a fixed line l and a fixed circle C not cutting it. A line m touching C becomes the other tangent m' to C from the cut of l, m. A line parallel to m becomes the line through its cut with l, parallel to m'. This is the *"Laguerre inversion"*.

It turns a circle into a circle, the two having l as the radical axis. A circle may shrink to a point, but may not open out to a line. It leaves the tangential interval of two circles invariant.

Any transformation of the subgroup resembling the group of displacements (the *"restricted"* Laguerre group), is the product of four Laguerre inversions, if direct, of three, if indirect.

We have theorems in this geometry which correspond to those in inversion geometry: The six-circles theorem, and that on four lines (§ 18) become: If $C_1, \ldots, C_4$ be circles, and t_{ij}, t'_{ij} the pair of common tangents of C_i, C_j, then if t_{12}, t_{23}, t_{34}, t_{41} touch a circle, so do t'_{12}, t'_{23}, t'_{34}, t'_{41}.

If $C_1, \ldots, C_4$ touch a line, and the other common tangents be t_{12}, and so on, then the circles which touch $t_{23}t_{34}t_{42}$, $t_{34}t_{41}t_{13}$, $t_{41}t_{12}t_{24}$, $t_{12}t_{23}t_{31}$ all touch a circle.

187. *Relativity.* All this extends to three, or more, dimensions. In three, we orient our planes and spheres, the former by giving a sense of rotation on them, the latter by giving signs to their radii. Two spheres with radii r, r' (positive or negative), whose centres are at a distance d apart, have $d^2 - (r - r')^2$ as the square of the tangential interval. If this vanishes, they touch, as oriented spheres.

The theory in three dimensions gives the geometry of the restricted relativity theory, for, if (x, y, z) and (x', y', z') be the centres of spheres of radii ct, ct', the tangential interval is invariant under the group of Lorentz transformations, and is the "interval" between the "events" (x, y, z, t) and (x', y', z', t'), and this group corresponds to the restricted Laguerre group above.

188. *Lines in space and points in five dimensional space.* A line in ordinary space with co-ordinates L, M, N, l, m, n, which now write $y_1, y_2, \ldots y_6$, can be represented by a point in five dimensions, with the y as homogeneous co-ordinates, provided $y_1y_4 + y_2y_5 + y_3y_6 = 0$. (§ 146.)

It is convenient to change the notation slightly, writing

$$x_1 = \tfrac{1}{2}(y_1 + y_4), \quad x_2 = \tfrac{1}{2}(y_2 + y_5), \quad x_3 = \tfrac{1}{2}(y_3 + y_6),$$
$$x_4 = \tfrac{1}{2}(y_1 - y_4), \quad x_5 = \tfrac{1}{2}(y_2 - y_5), \quad x_6 = \tfrac{1}{2}(y_3 - y_6).$$

The relation between the y then becomes

$$x_1^2 + x_2^2 + x_3^2 - x_4^2 - x_5^2 - x_6^2 = 0.$$

This is a quadric in five dimensions, if $x_1, \ldots, x_6$ be taken as homogeneous co-ordinates; points x, x' are conjugate if

$$x_1x'_1 + x_2x'_2 + x_3x'_3 - x_4x'_4 - x_5x'_5 - x_6x'_6 = 0,$$

and this turns out to be the condition that the corresponding lines cut. This fact dominates the sequel. If we subject the x to a linear condition, then L, M, N, l, m, n are subjected to a linear condition. Hence the lines of a linear complex correspond to the points of a four-dimensional section of the quadric by a prime. Similarly the lines of a linear congruence correspond to points of the cut of the quadric and a space of three dimensions; this space has a polar* line for the quadric, meeting the quadric in the two points which correspond to the directrices of the congruence.

The points in which a plane cuts the quadric, correspond to the lines of a regulus; the plane has a polar plane* for the

---

* Two figures are *"polar"* for a quadric when *any* point on one, and *any* point on the other are separated harmonically by the points where the join of the points cuts the quadric.

quadric, cutting the quadric in points which represent the lines of the opposite regulus.

Quadrics in three dimensions have two families of generator lines; quadrics in five dimensions are curved four dimensional structures, and have lying on them two families of planes; two of the *same* family meet in one point, two of an opposite family do not, in general, meet. Any two points on such a "generator plane" are conjugate, and hence correspond to two intersecting lines. The points on a generator of one family, correspond to coplanar lines. Those of a generator of the other family, correspond to concurrent lines.

Theorems on lines in space, e.g. the double-six theorem, can be turned into theorems on our quadric.

189. *The Lie Geometry* includes inversion geometry and the Laguerre geometry of three dimensions.

Write the equation of a sphere in the form

$$a_0(x^2 + y^2 + z^2) + 2(a_1x + a_2y + a_3z) + a_4 = 0.$$

Its radius r is a_5/a_0 (assuming $a_0 \neq 0$), where

$$a_5^2 = a_1^2 + a_2^2 + a_3^2 - a_0a_4 \qquad (1)$$

If $a_0, \ldots, a_4$ be given, there are two corresponding values of r, and hence we can orient our spheres and planes. *Suppose this done.*

Take $a_0, \ldots, a_5$ as homogeneous co-ordinates of the sphere, connected by (1). If $a_0 = 0$, they are co-ordinates of a plane, whose two orientations correspond to the two signs of a_5.

If now we regard $a_0, \ldots, a_5$ as homogeneous co-ordinates in five dimensions, the collineations which leave the quadric (1) invariant constitute the "*Lie group*".

Two spheres $(a_0, \ldots, a_5)$, $(a'_0, \ldots, a'_5)$ touch if

$$\left(\frac{a_1}{a_0} - \frac{a'_1}{a'_0}\right)^2 + \left(\frac{a_2}{a_0} - \frac{a'_2}{a'_0}\right)^2 + \left(\frac{a_3}{a_0} - \frac{a'_3}{a'_0}\right)^2 - \left(\frac{a_5}{a_0} - \frac{a'_5}{a'_0}\right)^2 = 0,$$

whence

$$a_1a'_1 + a_2a'_2 + a_3a'_3 - \tfrac{1}{2}(a_0a'_4 + a_4a'_0) - a_5a'_5 = 0,$$

and this is the condition that the corresponding points a, a' in the five-dimensional space are conjugate for the quadric (1).

The subgroup of inversion turns point-spheres into point-spheres, and hence leaves $a_5 = 0$ invariant; the (complete) Laguerre group turns planes into planes, and hence leaves $a_0 = 0$ invariant. The Lie group preserves tangency but treats planes, spheres, points on an equal footing.

Now comes an extraordinary correspondence. Write (1) as

$$a_1^2 + a_2^2 + a_3^2 - \tfrac{1}{4}(a_0 + a_4)^2 + \tfrac{1}{4}(a_0 - a_4)^2 - a_5^2 = 0;$$

the co-ordinates then satisfy a quadratic equation of the same dimension as that for the co-ordinates of a line in space.

Thence, if we take complex co-ordinates, we have a one-to-one correspondence between lines and spheres, intersecting lines corresponding to tangent (oriented) spheres (§ 187).

The lines of a regulus are those which meet three given lines; corresponding to these we have spheres touching three given spheres. Their envelope is a Dupin cyclide (§ 164), which hence corresponds to a regulus.

From the double-six theorem we get: If five spheres touch a given sphere, any four have another tangent sphere. The five so got touch another sphere. In particular, the inspheres of the five tetrahedra formed by five (oriented) planes, touch a sphere.

190. *The tetrahedral complex.* If we have a collineation in space with just four distinct self-corresponding points (the general case), forming the "fundamental" tetrahedron, the set of lines obtained by joining each point to its corresponding point, constitute a complex, the *"tetrahedral complex"*. This is a case of a *"quadratic complex"* i.e. the lines through a general point lie on a quadric cone, those in a general plane touch a conic. The lines of the tetrahedral complex are cut by the faces of the tetrahedron in a constant cross-ratio. All lines through a vertex of the fundamental tetrahedron, and all in a face, must be considered to be in the complex.

A special case makes the situation clearer. The poles of a fixed plane for a set of confocal quadrics lie on a line perpendicular to the plane. Such a line is called a *"Reye axis"* of each of the confocals. Just one quadric of the system touches the plane, and the axis corresponding to the plane is a normal to the confocal at the point of contact, and, unless it goes through the centre, it is not normal to any other confocal. The axes are thus the set of normals to the confocals; they cut the principal planes of the confocals in points P, Q, R such that PQ/QR is a constant ratio. Thus the fundamental tetrahedron now consists of the principal planes of the quadric and the plane at infinity. The lines of the complex which pass through a given point, lie on a quadric cone through the centre of the confocals.

If a top be spinning under gravity about a fixed point P, the spin can be round a fixed vertical axis only if the vertical line through P is a Reye axis of the gyration ellipsoid of the top, and the angular velocity is suitably adjusted. We are assuming the ellipsoid is not a spheroid. This is one of the few theorems about general unsymmetrical tops.

191. *Kummer's surface*. A general quadratic complex is a set of lines whose six co-ordinates are connected by an additional * quadratic relation. The lines through a point lie on a quadric cone, but for some points, the "*singular*" points, the cone becomes a pair of planes. The locus of these singular points is a "*Kummer surface*". The "*singular planes*" are those on which the conic enveloped by the lines of the complex is a point-pair; they touch the Kummer surface. This surface is a quartic surface with sixteen "*nodes*", points like the vertex of a double cone, and sixteen "*tropes*", or planes which touch it along a conic. Each trope contains six nodes, and they lie on a conic; through each node go six tropes, and they touch a quadric cone. Kummer proved these facts in 1864.

A quartic surface in ordinary space with fourteen nodes has an equation of form:

$$\sqrt{xx'} + \sqrt{yy'} + \sqrt{zz'} = 0 \qquad (1)$$

where $x, \ldots, z$ are linear functions of the four co-ordinates. It acquires an additional node if we impose a relation between $x, y, \ldots z'$:

$$ax + by + cz + a'x' + b'y' + c'z' = 0, \text{ where } aa' = bb' = cc', \quad (2)$$

and two additional nodes if we impose two such relations. We

* Recall that the co-ordinates of any line satisfy one quadratic equation (§§ 146, 188).

then have a Kummer surface. This suggests that we consider (1) as the equation of a locus in four dimensions with co-ordinates $x, \ldots, z'$ connected by $x + \ldots + z' = 0$. This is Segre's quartic, and its points on any tangent three-dimensional space satisfy an equation of form (2), and hence are on a Kummer surface.

The tangential equation of (1) regarded as a locus in four dimensions, is of form

$$u_1^3 + \ldots + u_6^3 = 0$$

where $u_1 + \ldots + u_6 = 0$; it can be written

$$(u_2 + u_3)(u_3 + u_1)(u_1 + u_2) + (u_5 + u_6)(u_6 + u_4)(u_4 + u_5) = 0$$

and in nine similar ways. This shews there are 15 double lines on the locus, and the cut by any three-dimensional space has 15 nodes.

The dual locus is the cubic in four dimensions:

$$x_1^3 + \ldots + x_6^3 = 0 \text{ with } x_1 + \ldots + x_6 = 0$$

It has 10 nodes and its section by a 3-dimensional space yields the general cubic surface in ordinary space.

A large domain of geometry can be unified under these headings and it has contact with other fields such as the wave surface in doubly refracting crystals and even with the electron theory of quantum mechanics.

CHAPTER XI

GENERAL SPACE

192. In his Habilitationschrift (1854) Riemann extended the differential geometry of surfaces to the n-dimensional case, and his work later attained great prominence in Einstein's gravitation theory (1915). We shall give some account of the geometrical side of the theory, but it will now not be possible even to sketch proofs.

For a co-ordinate system on a surface, we used a net-work of curves; in a three-dimensional space, we could use three families of surfaces which partition space into boxes with curved faces, and *any* angles. Confocal quadrics give a simple instance. Each point of space has then three non-homogeneous co-ordinates determined by the particular surfaces of the three families through it. As in the case of a surface, it is usually necessary to consider a region of space rather than space as a whole.

If we have a manifold (i.e. a piece or the whole of a space), of n dimensions, a point in a particular region of the manifold can be given by n non-homogeneous co-ordinates $x_1, \ldots, x_n$, supposed real, where different points of the region correspond to different sets $x_1, \ldots, x_n$; as a point varies continuously on the manifold, the co-ordinates, one or more, are to vary continuously. The exact meaning of continuity on the manifold is discussed later. The whole manifold will be given by a finite or infinite set of overlapping regions.

193. *Vectors.* If $(x_1, \ldots, x_n)$ and $(x_1 + dx_1, \ldots, x_n + dx_n)$ are the co-ordinates of two nearby points of the manifold, we may take the increments $dx_1, \ldots, dx_n$ as proportional to the co-ordinates of a vector ξ^i at the first point. (The superscript i is merely a mark like a subscript; it is more usual in this work.) The vector ξ^i has co-ordinates $\xi^{(1)}, \xi^{(2)}, \ldots, \xi^{(n)}$.

Thus dx_1 represents the vector $(\xi^{(1)}, 0, \ldots 0)$; and any vector at the point corresponds to $k_1 dx_1 + k_2\, dx_2 + \ldots k_n dx_n$, for suitable constants $k_1, \ldots, k_n$.

If we take another co-ordinate system $y_1, \ldots, y_n$, where y_i is a continuous function of $x_1, \ldots, x_n$, then

$$dy_i = \Sigma \frac{\delta y_i}{\delta x_k} \, dx_k \qquad (1)$$

where, as always, the sum is over $1, 2, \ldots, n$ for each repeated letter, in subscript or superscript. We suppose that the determinant of the coefficients $\delta y_i / \delta x_k$ is not zero; then $y_1, \ldots, y_n$ are *independent* functions of $x_1, \ldots, x_n$, as they must be if they can be used as co-ordinates. Also, and this is very important, the co-ordinates of a vector at a point undergo a *linear* transformation, indicated by (1), when the change is made.

194. *Affine Connection.* Unless we can relate the vectors at different points, the manifold will be quite amorphous.

Consider a solid moving in space, and at any one of its points take three independent vectors; we can make vectors at different points of space correspond when they are connected by the motion. A more general case is given if we take a deformable compressible jelly instead of a solid.

The most obvious way to make vectors at P correspond to vectors at a *nearby* point P is to make those with equal co-ordinates correspond. This would make the correspondence depend on the particular co-ordinates used, instead of on the geometry of the manifold, but as a change of co-ordinates induces only a linear transformation of the co-ordinates of a vector at a point, this objection is removed if we assume:

The vector with co-ordinates ξ^i at P corresponds to that with co-ordinates $\xi^i + d\xi^i$ at P' where $d\xi^i$ is a linear function of the ξ^i. The vector $d\xi^i$ will depend also on the displacement from P to P'. We suppose P, P' are nearby points so that this displacement is dx_s, and then we may assume that $d\xi^i$ is a linear function of the vector whose co-ordinates are dx_s,

$$d\xi^i = -\Sigma \; \Gamma^{\;i}_{rs} \, \xi^r \, dx_s. \qquad (2)$$

Herein $\Gamma^{\;i}_{rs}$ may be any continuous functions of $x_1, \ldots, x_n$; when these *"coefficients of affine connection"* are known or assigned, we have the correspondence between vectors at nearby points. We assume that, by choice of suitable co-ordinates we could make these Γ vanish when we go from a *fixed* point P to nearby points, but this does not imply that we can make them vanish throughout a region.

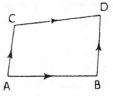

Fig. 118

195. *Transport.* We say that the vector ξ^i at P is "*transported*" to $\xi^i + d\xi^i$ at P', if (2) holds. Let the infinitesimal AB representing a vector at A be transported to CD at C. Compare this with the transport of AC, a vector at A, to a vector at B. We want the latter vector to be BD, so that $ABDC$ is a deformed "parallelogram". The condition for this is

$$\Gamma_{rs}^{\ i} = \Gamma_{sr}^{\ i} \tag{3}$$

196. *Geodesics* can be defined as curves whose tangent vectors, when transported along the curve, undergo the change given by (2). If the co-ordinates x_i of points on the curve be given as functions of a parameter t, so that $v^i = dx_i/dt$ is the tangent vector, this gives the equation

$$dv^i + \Sigma \, \Gamma_{jk}^{\ i} \, v^j dx_k = 0$$

or

$$\frac{d^2x_i}{dt^2} + \Sigma \, \Gamma_{jk}^{\ i} \, \frac{dx_j}{dt} \, \frac{dx_k}{dt} = 0.$$

Thus if P is on the curve, we can take a co-ordinate system near P so that the curve has equation $v^i = $ const. near P. These geodesics correspond, as far as is possible, to straight lines of ordinary space.

197. *The Riemannian.* Affinely connected space can be used as a foundation of the tensor calculus, but for Einstein's gravitation theory more is needed. Following Riemann, we assume there are infinitesimal distances in the manifold, and that the distance ds between nearby points is given by

$$ds^2 = \Sigma \, g_{ij} dx_i dx_j \quad (g_{ij} = g_{ji}) \tag{4}$$

where g_{ij} are continuous functions of $(x_1, \ldots, x_n)$. We then call the manifold a "*Riemannian*".

This is a generalization of the ds^2 for surface theory; the letter g for the coefficients became popular after Einstein had applied the method to his gravitation theory. We shall assume, what is not true in that theory, that ds^2 is *positive definite*, i.e. always positive unless all $dx_1, \ldots, dx_n$ vanish.

The functions g_{ij} give all the metric properties of the manifold. Thus if $(dx_1, \ldots, dx_n)$ and $(\delta x_1, \ldots, \delta x_n)$ be two vectors at the same point, the angle θ between them is given by

$$\cos \theta = \frac{\Sigma g_{ij} \, dx_i \, \delta x_j}{\sqrt{\Sigma g_{ij} dx_i dx_j} \; \sqrt{\Sigma g_{ij} \delta x_i \delta x_j}}$$

We now assume that among possible systems of transport of vectors, there is one which leaves the ds^2 of a vector unchanged. The corresponding Γ are then given by

$$\Gamma^i_{rs} = \Sigma g^{ij} \Gamma_{j, \, rs}$$

where $\Gamma_{j,rs} = \frac{1}{2}(g_{jr/s} + g_{js/r} - g_{rs/j})$, $g_{jk/l} = \delta g_{jk}/\delta x_l$ and g^{ij} is the co-factor of g_{ij} in the matrix of the g_{ij}, divided by the determinant of the matrix.

We can now define the length of a finite arc of a curve, and prove that the geodesic defined above is the shortest arc joining two points, not too far apart.

198. *Curvature.* Return to affinely connected space, and consider the "parallelogram" $ABDC$; if we transport the vector ξ^i round $ABDC$ from A back to A, it can be shewn by an argument like that used to prove Stokes' theorem, that it does not return to its original position, but undergoes a change depending on the infinitesimal area and orientation of the parallelogram:

$$d\xi^i = \frac{1}{2}\Sigma F^i_k, \, _{\alpha\beta} \, (\varDelta x)^{\alpha\beta} \, \xi^k,$$

where $(\varDelta x)^{\alpha\beta}$ is the area of the projection of the parallelogram on the planar direction given by dx^α, dx^β, and

$$F^i_k, \, _{\alpha\beta} = \frac{\delta \Gamma^i_{k\alpha}}{\delta x_\beta} - \frac{\delta \Gamma^i_{k\beta}}{\delta x_\alpha} + \Sigma(\Gamma^r_{k\alpha} \, \Gamma^i_{r\beta} - \Gamma^r_{k\beta} \, \Gamma^i_{r\alpha}).$$

We have

$$F^i_{k, \, \alpha\beta} + F^i_{\alpha, \, \beta k} + F^i_{\beta, k\alpha} = 0, \; F^i_{k, \, \alpha\beta} = -F^i_{k, \, \beta\alpha}$$

In a Riemannian we have also
$$F_{ik,\alpha\beta} = -F_{ki,\alpha\beta},$$
where
$$F_{ik,\alpha\beta} = \Sigma g_{ri} F^r_{k,\alpha\beta}.$$
$F_{ik,\alpha\beta}$ is the *"curvature tensor"*; it is a generalization of the notion of the curvature of a surface, and very important in Einstein's theory.

For example, let $z = f(x, y)$ be the equation of a surface in ordinary space, with a point on it as origin. Near the origin, if we expand $f(x, y)$ in powers of x, y, the surface has an equation of form
$$z = px + qy + \text{terms of higher degree},$$
also, near the origin
$$p = \delta z/\delta x, \quad q = \delta z/\delta y, \quad dz = pdx + qdy,$$
$$ds^2 = dx^2 + dy^2 + (pdx + qdy)^2$$
$$= (1 + p^2)dx^2 + 2pq\, dx\, dy + (1 + q^2)dy^2.$$
We find that $F_{12,12}$ is the total curvature of the surface at the origin.

199. *Homogeneous Space.* A space will be *"isotropic"* at a point if the change in ξ^i, produced by a circuit of a "parallelogram", is independent of the orientation of the parallelogram. Calculation then shews that, at that point
$$-F_{ik,\alpha\beta} = \lambda(g_{i\alpha}g_{k\beta} - g_{i\beta}g_{k\alpha}).$$
λ is called the *"curvature"* of the space at the point.

If the space is isotropic at *all* points of a region, then λ is constant in the region, by a surprising theorem of Schur's, and the region is of constant curvature, and is a portion of Euclidean, elliptic, or hyperbolic space (of n dimensions), according as λ is zero, positive, or negative. Let us call these homogeneous spaces *"classical"*. The last two cases are merely n-dimensional extensions of the geometries considered in Chapter V.

200. *Helmholtz' problem.* We wish to characterize this homogeneous space (or region), geometrically. Consider a manifold which has a distance formula of form $ds = f(dx_1, \ldots, dx_n)$, where the only assumption on f is that it is homogeneous of the first order, so that $kds = f(kdx_1, \ldots, kdx_n)$ for all constants k. Thus the fourth power of ds might be a polynomial of degree four in $dx_1, \ldots, dx_n$. The f's at different points are to be connected, as in a Riemannian, by linear homogeneous transformations of the dx_i, so that the space is affinely connected.

We now assume a generalization of the properties of rigid motion, called *"free mobility in the infinitesimal"*. Taking three dimensions for simplicity, the assumption is: There is a congruent mapping (i.e. a mapping which preserves ds unchanged), of vectors at a point P on vectors at the same or another point P', which carries any given direction l at P, into any given direction l' at P', and if these P, P', l, l' be given, it carries any given planar direction (given by two directions) through l into any through l'. If all these correspondences be given, the mapping is required to be unique.

A lengthy and difficult argument proves that: (1) if we apply this free mobility to vectors at the same point, then ds^2 is a positive definite quadratic in $dx_1, \ldots, dx_n$ (§ 196); (2) if we apply it to all pairs of distinct points, then the manifold is homogeneous.

Thus a homogeneous space or manifold is characterized geometrically.

201. *Planes*. If a surface in a space be such that any geodesic of the space, through two points of the surface, lies entirely on the surface, we may call the surface a *"plane"*. In general a Riemannian does not contain such surfaces. But if we assume that given any point, and any two infinitesimal directions there, we can always draw a "plane" through the point containing these directions, this assumption is equivalent to that of free mobility. Either condition is a necessary and sufficient condition that the Riemannian can be mapped on a (portion of) Euclidean space, so that its geodesics correspond to straight lines. This resembles Beltrami's theorem in § 158.

202. *Local and Global*. We again mention that, notwithstanding any appearances to the contrary, we have been concerned only with local properties, properties in a region which may be very large, and not with global properties which concern the whole manifold.

Thus, for instance, even the surface of a sphere cannot be provided with a system of co-ordinates regular everywhere, and such that the correspondence between points and co-ordinates is one-to-one.

A domain on a surface of a cylinder, or on one sheet of a cone, if not too large a domain, has the same intrinsic geometry as a portion of a plane. But globally they differ. The cone has a singular point, its vertex; such points we completely exclude. When we develop the cylinder on a plane, either we may use only an (infinite) strip of the plane, or we may repeat the strip so that to each point on the cylinder corresponds an infinite number of points on the plane, but to a point on the plane, only one on the cylinder. Similarly for the cone; we may use either a circular sector, or if the angle of the cone is incommensurable with a right angle, we may use a covering of the plane an infinite number of times.

Just as a cylinder or cone can be developed on a plane, so a locally homogeneous space (§ 198) can be developed on the corresponding classical non-Euclidean space (or a Euclidean space), and this development can be made to cover all the space just once, provided we make an assumption which excludes the cases analogous to the cone. If we remove the vertex from the cone, we can have an infinite set of points on it, which has no limit point (see below, the limit point would be the vertex, if it were still there); similarly on a cylinder a set of points may have no limit point, but then the set is not contained in a bounded region.

We say that a manifold is *"finitely compact"* if any infinite sequence $P_1, P_2 \ldots$ of points in a *bounded* region has a *"limit point"* P in the manifold, that is, a point such that any region which includes P, however small, includes an infinite number of points of the sequence. The assumption to which we referred a moment ago is that our manifold is finitely compact.

203. *Locally homogeneous spaces.* Conversely, in a classical homogeneous space we can construct models of other locally homogeneous spaces.

Consider in Euclidean space, with rectangular axes, the translations with components (h_1a_1, h_2a_2, h_3a_3) along the axes, where a_1, a_2, a_3 are constants, and h_1, h_2, h_3 integers of either sign. These displacements form a group. A box with edges of lengths a_1, a_2, a_3 is a *"fundamental region"* of the group, which means that any point of space can be derived from a point of this region by an operation of the group, and that two points of the region are never connected by such an operation. We must assume that of two opposite faces of the box, only one is supposed to be contained in the region.

If we identify any point of the fundamental region with all those derived from it by operations of the group, we get a locally Euclidean space. Or we can regard the fundamental region as a model of such a space, where we identify points on its boundary which are connected by operations of the group. Compare this with the representation of a cylinder by points on a strip of a plane, and with the representation of a Clifford surface by points of a rectangular area (§ 107). This locally Euclidean space is of *finite volume*.

Generally any discontinuous group of transformations, preserving distance, of a classical homogeneous space, can be used to give a model of a locally homogeneous space, provided that no element of the group (except identity), leaves any point fixed.

204. *Topology* must be referred to if we wish a clearer view. This topic deals with the properties of figures which are unchanged by any one-to-one correspondence of points which is continuous both ways; that is, if the point P corresponds to Q, and P varies continuously, so does Q, and conversely. Figures connected by such a correspondence are "*homeomorphic*". Thus if we deform a surface and allow stretching and compression as well as bending, but not folding or tearing, we get a homeomorphic surface. A sphere with one point missing is homeomorphic to a circular disc with its circumference omitted, and, as stereographic projection (§ 25) shews, it is also homeomorphic to an infinite plane (with no line at infinity).

On a sphere any circuit can be shrunk continuously to a point. On an anchor ring (Fig. 93), this is not the case for the circuits shewn. An anchor ring is not homeomorphic to a sphere.

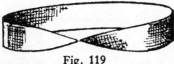

Fig. 119

More unexpected are the "Möbius leaf" and the "Klein bottle". The leaf is made by taking a strip of paper and gumming the ends together after turning one round through 180° (Fig. 119). If two opposite points on the sheet, one on each side, be identified, we have a model of a one-sided surface. It is homeomorphic to a strip extending right across an elliptic plane, and this explains why a line does not separate such a plane (p. 99).

The Klein bottle is a one-sided tube. If a tube pierces itself as in Fig. 120, and we connect the outer tube with the inner

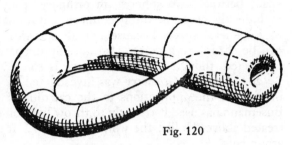

Fig. 120

by a cap stretching across the gap, we have the bottle.

A two-dimensional locally Euclidean space may be homeomorphic to a plane, cylinder, anchor ring, Möbius leaf or Klein bottle. (We must think of the leaf as made from a strip of infinite breadth.) There are no other types. For two-dimensional locally hyperbolic geometry, there is an infinite number of types: they are connected with Poincaré's automorphic functions.

For higher dimensions, the study of different topological types is very difficult. For locally hyperbolic geometries, the number of distinct types is infinite, but for locally Euclidean finite; for locally elliptic space of an *even* number of dimensions, there are but two types, one corresponding to spherical, the other to elliptic space; for an odd number of dimensions, there are more types. The geometry of a spherical space is that of a hypersphere immersed in a Euclidean space of one more dimension.

We shall soon see that a locally homogeneous space is a classical space when only one line can be drawn through two given points. The fact that this assumption does not hold for all spaces above, loses its strangeness, if we note that through two points on a cylinder, an infinite number of geodesics can be drawn, if we allow them to wind round the cylinder.

A space of non-positive curvature, constant or not, is homeomorphic to Euclidean space, and hence is classical if its curvature is constant, provided it is simply connected, that is, if any closed circuit on it, can be shrunk continuously to a point. To give significance to this statement, we may note that the space between two spheres, in ordinary space, one of which includes the other, is simply connected, but not homeomorphic to Euclidean space, because not all spherical surfaces in it can be shrunk to a point; also an elliptic space is not simply connected, though a spherical space is so.

205. *Distance Geometry* was investigated by Menger, partly in view of the applications to the calculus of variations, but Busemann has used it recently to throw light on some questions treated above. Unlike the work in Chap. VI, it uses continuity arguments.

We take, as undefined, the "*distance*" between each pair of points A, B. This is a real number, denoted by AB, which satisfies

(1) $AB = 0$ if, and only if, $A = B$,
(2) $AB + AC \geqq BC$.

It then easily follows that

$$AB = BA, \quad AB \geqq 0, \quad AB + BC \geqq AC.$$

If the equality sign holds in the last formula, we say B is "*between*" A and C, and write (ABC). We can deduce those properties mentioned in § 115 which involve only three points, and further that (ABC), (ACD) hold if, and only if, (ABD), (BCD) hold.

But we cannot shew that (ABC), (BCD) together imply (ABD), for this is false for points equally spaced on a circle, though the assumptions hold, with an obvious interpretation of "between".

As our distances are real numbers, we can define a "*limit point*" of a sequence P_1, P_2, ... as a point P, if it exists, such that PP_r tends to zero as r tends to infinity. A sequence cannot have two distinct limit points.

A set of points is "*bounded*" if the distance between each pair of points of the set is less than some definite real number; a space is "*finitely compact*" if each bounded sequence of points in the space has a subsequence with a limit point in the space. (This is the present version of the property described by the same name above.)

A space is *"convex"* if, when A, B are any points, there is a point X such that (AXB) holds.

We assume henceforth that our space is convex and finitely compact.

There is a risk that the reader will not realize the great generality of this theory. It may help him if he thinks of space as filled with media of varying refractive indices, and takes the "distance" between two points to be the shortest time in which light could travel from one to the other.

We define an *"interval"* $<PQ>$, and a *"continuous arc"* from P to Q as a set of points in one-to-one correspondence with the set of real numbers between two numbers t_1, t_2 (including t_1, t_2), such that:

(1) If X, Y be on the *interval*, and x, y the corresponding numbers, then the distance xy is the difference between x and y,

(2) If X_r tends to X, by a sequence of points along the *arc*, then the corresponding x_r tend to the corresponding x.

We do not assert that an interval $<PQ>$ exists, or is unique, for every pair P, Q.

We can, however, define the *"length"* of a continuous arc, and prove that if there is one of finite length from P to Q, there is also one whose length is not greater than any other, and that this is *an* interval $<PQ>$; and, further, that if (PXQ), then there is an interval $<PQ>$ which contains X, and that, if Y, Z be on it, then either (PYZ) or (ZYQ). The order relations of § 115 then hold for points on $<PQ>$.

206. *A congruence axiom.* To get a space of a more usual type we assume that we can cut off given lengths if they are not too great. More exactly, we assume:

If P is any point, there is a number ρ such that if points A, B be distinct and PA, $PB < \rho$, then there is just one point C such that $BC = \delta$, $AB + BC = AC$, provided δ be small enough.

A *"geodesic"* is defined as a map of the whole real axis,

which is locally faithful; that is, $P(t)$ runs over the whole geodesic (perhaps more than once), when the real number t runs through all real values, and further, if t be given, there is a neighbourhood round it, such that if t_1, t_2 be in it then:

The distance from $P(t_1)$ to $P(t_2)$ is the difference between t_1 and t_2. It can now be proved that, if P, Q be two given points, and $<PQ>$ an interval between them, then there is just one geodesic which contains this interval; and that two geodesics can meet in only a finite number or an enumerable* number of points.

The geodesics which will interest us are those which are *"congruent maps"* of Euclidean straight lines and circles; that is, the distance between two points of the geodesic equals that between the corresponding points of the Euclidean figure. As the straight line in elliptic space is the congruent map of a Euclidean circle, we will call both kinds of geodesics "lines".

It can be shewn that a geodesic is a line, if and only if, it contains an interval $<XY>$, whenever it contains X, Y; and that if two distinct lines meet in just two points A, B they are closed, have equal lengths, and each contains two intervals $<AB>$. Compare great circles on a sphere.

207. *Lines unique.* Suppose now any two points lie on at most one (and therefore just one), geodesic. It can then be proved that either all geodesics are congruent maps of Euclidean straight lines, or all are congruent maps of one Euclidean circle, and accordingly all have the same length. We call the spaces *"open"* and *"closed"* respectively.

In the first case, space is simply-connected; in the second, it is not, but it may be obtained from a simply-connected space which (like the sphere), has the property that all geodesics through any one point pass through another. We get the space when we identify these "opposite" points. This is a highly remarkable result, in view of the slender axiom-basis which leads to it. It is due to Busemann.

If the space is closed, and of at least three dimensions, we can ensure that it is an *elliptic space* if we further assume

* An enumerable set is one which can be put into one-to-one correspondence with the set of all the natural numbers.

that a line and a sphere cannot meet in more than two points; or, if we assume that the space is symmetric about each of its points, or about each of its lines.

For open spaces, such assumptions do not suffice to give homogeneous space.

208. *Free mobility.* We may define a motion as a one-to-one transformation of points which preserves distances and is direct. Then if we assume:

(1) If each point P has a neighbourhood such that if the distances PA, PB, AB equal PA', PB', $A'B'$ respectively, then there is a motion of the neighbourhood on itself which turns P, A, B into P, A', B', it follows that space is locally homogeneous.

(2) If whenever the distances AC, BC equal AC', BC', there is a motion of space which turns A, B, C into A, B, C', it follows that the space is a classical homogeneous space.

This corresponds to the solution of Helmholtz' problem in the present theory. It would not be enough to assume that if $AB = A'B'$ there is a motion turning A, B into A', B', for there is a four-dimensional Riemannian where this holds, although the space is non-homogeneous.

209. *Metric Topology.* We have assumed that each pair of points has a distance satisfying § 205 (1) (2). We consider the deeper conditions that this should be the case.

As our spaces are often locally defined, let us begin with the undefined notions of "*point*" and "*neighbourhood of a point*", a certain class of points. We assume

(1) Any neighbourhood of P contains P.

(2) If P is in a neighbourhood of Q, then Q is in a neighbourhood of P.

(3) If P is in the neighbourhoods U and V, there is neighbourhood of P contained in both U and V.

(4) If P, Q are distinct points, there is a neighbourhood of P which does not contain Q.

A point P is a "*limit point*" of a set M, if each neighbourhood of P contains a point of M distinct from P. If we adjoin to M all its limit points we get the "*closure*" of M.

(5) If V is any neighbourhood of P, there is another whose closure is contained in V.

(6) There is a sequence of neighbourhoods $R_1, R_2 \ldots$ such that at least one is contained in any given neighbourhood of any given point, and contains that point.

It can be shewn that on a set of points satisfying these axioms, a distance can be defined satisfying (1) (2) of § 205, and such that the distance XY is a continuous function of X, Y.

That is, if $X_1, X_2, \ldots$ is a sequence of points whose limit point is X, and $Y_1, Y_2, \ldots$ a sequence of points whose limit point is Y, then the distance $X_n Y_n$ tends to the distance XY, as n tends to infinity.

The preceding sections then add more and more assumptions giving geometries of more special kinds until the homogeneous spaces are reached.

REFERENCES

THERE are many books on the subject matter of the first chapter. Those nearest the present treatment are Forder, *Higher Course Geometry*, and Roger Johnson, *Modern Geometry*. For co-ordinate geometry of the conic see, for a modern treatment, Robson, *Introduction to Analytical Geometry*. Other books are Sommerville, *Analytical Conics*, and the famous classic, Salmon, *Conic Sections*. For three dimensions R. J. T. Bell, *Co-ordinate Geometry of Three Dimensions*, is a well-known introduction.

A general survey of questions on the axioms of Geometry will be found in de B. Robinson, *The Foundations of Geometry*; for special topics: Coxeter, *The Real Projective Plane*; Veblen and Young, *Projective Geometry*; Forder, *Foundations of Euclidean Geometry*.

Further developments on projective and co-ordinate geometry will be found in the recent books: Todd, *Projective and Analytical Geometry*; Hodge and Pedoe, *Methods of Algebraic Geometry*. In particular, the latter connects up the subject with modern algebra. For the latter subject see D. E. Littlewood's book in this series. Baker's *Principles of Geometry*, Vols. I–IV, and his *Introduction to Plane Geometry* are a mine of information and elegant treatment from the plane to higher dimensions.

Coxeter, *Non Euclidean Geometry*, and the earlier book of Sommerville with the same title, contain fascinating accounts of the subject.

On higher plane curves, Wieleitner's little books *Algebraische Kurven* in the *Sammlung Göschen* are packed with material, some of which we have used. More advanced and dealing with the Italian theory is Coolidge, *Algebraic Plane Curves*. The recent book, Semple and Roth, *Algebraic Geometry*, and Baker, *Principles*, V, VI, include also a study of surfaces.

The classical treatment of differential geometry is in the four large volumes: Darboux, *Leçons sur la Théorie Générale des Surfaces*.

For an introduction see Eisenhart, *Differential Geometry*; Weather-burn, *Differential Geometry* (2 vols.), and the extremely elegant treatment in Blaschke, *Differentialgeometrie I*. Vol. III of the latter book deals in detail with the Laguerre and Lie Geometries.

A connected account of Busemann's work will be found in his *Geometry of Geodesics*. An introduction to this is Busemann and Kelly: *Projective Geometry and Projective Metrics*, which considers other types of non-Euclidean geometry as well as those in this book. Some of the other topics in the last chapter are treated in Weyl, *Mathematische Analyse des Raumproblems*, and Cartan, *La Géométrie des Espaces de Riemann*.

A bird's-eye view of the whole subject is found in Coolidge, *History of Geometrical Methods*.

INDEX

ABSOLUTE, 92
Affine, theorems, 76, 108
—— connection, 180
Anchor ring, 137
Angle of parallelism, 82
Antinversion, 20
Areas, 108
Argand diagram, 27, 169
Astroid, 34, 159
Asymptote, 31
—— of conic, 49
—— inflexional, 32
Asymptotic directions on surface, 135
—— lines, 136
—— triangle, 86
Axiom, 56
—— D, 60, 64
—— Euclidean, 80, 112
—— F, 64
—— H, 81
—— P, 65
—— of Archimedes, 107, 109
—— of congruence, 97, 189
—— of distance, 188
—— of Fano, 63
—— of order, 100, 103
—— of projective geometry, 58, 79
—— of Veblen, 102
—— circle, 100

BEAK on curve, 162
Bilinear form, 45

Binormal, 131
Bitangent, 33, 151
Branch of curve, 160
—— cycle of, 160
Bundle, 70, 104, 124

CARDIOID, 33, 157
Catenary, 36
—— directrix of, 36
Catenoid, 137, 144
Circle, at infinity, 120
—— coaxal, 23, 27, 41
—— cutting diametrically, 27
—— director, 50
—— oriented, 171
—— orthogonal, 22, 27
Circular points at infinity, I, J, 50
Class, of cubic, 155
—— of curve, 152
Clifford, parallel, surface, 93
Collineation, 41, 77, 117, 168
—— degenerate, 41
—— group, 41
Complex, linear, 127, 174
—— quadratic, 176
—— tetrahedral, 176
Conic, 30, 67
—— apolar, 53, 157
—— centre of, 48, 74
—— diameter of, 48
—— directrix, eccentricity, focus of, 30, 51
—— focal, 123

CONIC, (contd.)
—— principal axes of, 49, 51
—— envelope, 70
—— locus, 67
Confocal, conics, 51, 54
—— quadrics, 122
Congruent, 9, 96
Congruence, linear, 129, 174
—— directrices of, 130
—— normal, 147
—— foci, focal surface, limiting
        points of, 147, 148
Conjugate, diameters of conic,
        48, 74
—— point, line for conic, 45
—— for quadric, 120, 168
—— for linear complex, 129
Continuity, continuum, 111
Correspondence, in bundles, 125
—— one-to-one, 57
—— projective, 118
Cross-ratio, 43, 118, 169
Cubic, curve, 31, 151
—— envelope, 154, 156
—— surface, 125
—— twisted, 126, 131
Curve, adjoint, 165
—— reducible, nonsingular, 152
—— unicursal, 159
Curvature, of curve, 35, 132,
        135 f.n.
—— of ellipse, 37
—— of quadric, 140
—— centre, radius of, 35
—— geodesic, 143
—— principal, 135
—— total, 139
—— tensor, 183
Cusp, 32, 150
—— Cuspidal edge, 138
Cyclide, 148, 176
Cycloid, 35

DEFECT of triangle, 84
Definition, 57
Deformation of surfaces, 139,
        146
Developable surfaces, 139
Direction cosines, 115
Displacement, 11
—— indirect, 13
—— in space, 24
Double point, 32
Double-six, 126
Duality, in plane, 48, 60
—— in space, 79

ELLIPSE, 30
—— ellipsoid, 116
Envelope, 34
—— of spheres, 147, 148
Epicycloid, 33
Equivalence, by addition, 84, 108
—— of volumes, 108
Evolute, 35
Erlanger Programme, 113

Field, a set of elements obeying
        the laws of ordinary
        algebra for addition, sub-
        traction, multiplication,
        and division, 76
—— finite, 78
Flex, 31, 151
—— of cubic curve, 152, 156

GENERATORS of quadrics, 118
Genus of curve, 158
Geodesic, 140, 181, 189

GEODESIC, (*contd.*)
—— on quadrics 146
Geometry, congruence, 103
—— descriptive, 103
—— distance, 188
—— elliptic, 92;
—— Euclidean, 73, 77, 107
—— finite projective, 59
—— hyperbolic, 81
—— inversion, 29
—— Laguerre, 172
—— Lie, 175
—— ordered projective, 105
—— spherical, 92
Group, 12
—— abelian, 13;
—— Laguerre, 172
—— Lie, 175
Gauge constructions, 110

HARMONIC, conic locus, 53
—— homology, 72, 121
—— — pencil, range, 43, 62
—— polar for cubic curve, 156
Helicoid, 144
Helix, 132
Helmholtz' problem, 183, 191
Hessian, 154
Homogeneous co-ordinates, in plane, 39
—— in space, 117
—— — of line in plane, 43
—— in space, 127
—— of plane, 117
—— of prime, 168
Homothety, centre, ratio of, 14
Homeomorphic, 186
Horocycle, 85
Hyperbola, 30
—— — rectangular, 49, 50

Hyperboloid, 116
Hypocycloid, 157

IMAGE of point in line, 9
Imaginary, points, 42, 120
—— lines, 44
—— conic, 44, 120
Inversion, 19, 52
—— centre, radius of, 19
—— Laguerre, 173
—— in space, 25
—— plane, 29
Involute, 35
Involution, 71
—— bi-axial, 121, 171
—— Möbius, 170
—— pencil in, 71
—— product of, 72;
—— on conic, 71
Isotropic, lines, 50
—— cone, 120

JACOBIAN, 157

KLEIN'S equation, 156
—— bottle, 187

LIMIT, point, 185, 188
—— rays, 82
—— triangle, 83
Limiting points of coaxal systems, 23
Line, at infinity, 39, 73
—— of curvature on surface, 136

LINE, (contd.)
—— on quadric, 146
—— oriented, 171
—— parallel, 39, 73
Line co-ordinates, 127

MOBILITY, free, 184
Möbius pairs, 27, 119
—— leaf, 186
Models of non-euclidean geo-
    metry, 90, 91, 92

NET, of conics, 153, 157
—— of quadrics, 122
Nine point circle, 16, 52
Node of curve, 32, 150
Normal, to conic, 54
—— to curve, 35
—— to surface, 134
—— plane to curve, 131
—— principal, 131
Null, system, 128, 132, 168
—— plane, point, 128

ORDER, of curve, 151
—— of singularity, 162
Orthocentre, 15
—— orthocentric points, 15, 50,
    52
Oscnode, cusp, 162
Osculating plane, 131

PARABOLA, 18, 49, 74;
—— directrix, focus, vertex, 30

Parabolic point of surface, 136
Paraboloid, elliptic, hyperbolic,
    116
Pencil, 41, 59
—— centre of, 59
—— of planes, 105, 118, 125
—— of lines in hyperbolic geo-
        metry, 82, 84
—— of quadrics, 122
Perspective, ranges, pencils, 61,
    62
Plane, 79, 102, 184
—— at infinity, 117
Plücker equations, 154
Point at infinity, 39
—— dependent, 167
—— isolated, 32
—— reference, 167
Polar, figures for quadric, 174
—— prime, 168
Polar, of line, for quadric, 120
—— for sphere, 26
—— of point, for conic, 45, 69
—— for curve, 153
—— for quadric, 120
Polarity, 168
Pole of line for conic, 45, 69
Prime, 168
Principal axes of conic, 49
—— planes of surface at a point,
        135
Projective co-ordinates, 74, 76
—— generation of quadrics and
        cubic surfaces, 124
—— ranges, pencils, 62, 164
—— range on conic, 71
Projectivity, 62
Pseudo-sphere, 142

QUADRANGLE, 61
Quadric locus, 115, 168

QUADRIC, (*contd*.)
—— envelope, 124
Quadrilateral, 61
Quartic curve, 32, 121
—— Kummer's, 177
—— Segre's, 178
Quasifield, a set of elements obeying the laws of a field, except the commutative law of multiplication, 76
—— ordered, 106

RADICAL axis, 23, 41
—— centre, 42
Range of points, 59
Reciprocal of conic, 52
Reflection, in line, 9, 25
—— in plane, 24
—— in point, 13
Regular point of surface, 133
Regulus, 118
—— opposite, 118
Relativity theory, 173
—— of gravitation, 179, 181
Residual sets, 165
Reye axis, 176
Riemannian, 181
Rotation, 10
—— in space, 24
Ruled quadrics, 118
—— surfaces, 139 f.n., 147

SCREW, 25
Self-polar, triangle, 47, 69, 73, 153
—— tetrahedron, 121
—— reference figure, 169

Similar, 9, 107
Similitude, 16
—— centre of, 14
—— direct, 16
Simson line, 17, 34, 158
Singular point, singularity, 32
—— of curve, 150
—— of surface, 134
—— ordinary singularities of curve, 163
Space, classical, isotropic, 198
—— elliptic, 190
Spherical representation of curve, 132
—— of surface, 139
Spinning top, 177
Statics, 130
Stereographic projection, 26
Surface, of constant curvature, 141
—— of constant mean curvature, 145
—— minimal, 144, 145
—— screw, 145

TACNODE, 162
Tangent, to conic, 68
—— to parabola, 18
Tangent plane, to quadric, 119
—— to surface, 133
Tangential equation, 47
Theorem, criss-cross, 72
—— double six, 126, 176
—— eight circles, 21
—— on four lines, 17, 22, 50, 173
—— fundamental—of projective geometry, 64
—— pivot, 17, 152
—— six circles, 20, 122, 165, 173

Theorem of, Apollonius, 54
—— Beltrami, 143, 147, 184
—— Bolyai, 86
—— Lobatchefsky, 89
—— Bonnet, 143
—— Bour, 145
—— Brianchon, 70, 119
—— Busemann, 190
—— Desargues, 60, 71
—— Dorroh, 100
—— Dupin, 137, 147
—— Gauss, 111
—— Graves, 55
—— Hesse, 171
—— Hilbert, 85, 86, 111
—— Kummer, 177
—— Liouville, 138, 171
—— Malus, 147
—— Morley-Petersen, 171
—— Noether, 164, 166
—— Pappus, 65, 75, 106, 119
—— Pascal, 68, 73, 152
—— Poncelet, 55
—— Pythagoras, 108
—— Saccheri, 83
—— Schur, 183
—— Serret-Frenet, 132
—— Soddy, 26
—— Steiner, 23, 54
—— Wedderburn, 78

—— Weyl, 143
Topology, 186
Torse, 138
Torsion, 132
—— radius of, 132
Tractrix, 36, 142
Transformation, inverse of, 12
—— birational, 165
—— circular, 28, 169
—— conformal, 138
—— Cremona, 166
—— direct, 10
—— linear fractional, 28
—— product of, 10
—— projective, 62, 77, 168
—— quadratic, 51, 158
Translation, 10
—— in space, 24
Transport, 181

Umbilic, 135
—— on quadrics, 144
Uniformization of curve, 159
Undefined terms, 58

Volumes, 109

HARPER TORCHBOOKS / The Bollingen Library

Rachel Bespaloff	ON THE ILIAD. Introduction by Hermann Broch TB/2006
Elliott Coleman, *ed.*	LECTURES IN CRITICISM: *By R. P. Blackmur, B. Croce, Henri Peyre, John Crowe Ransom, Herbert Read, and Allen Tate* TB/2003
C. G. Jung	PSYCHOLOGICAL REFLECTIONS. Edited by Jolande Jacobi TB/2001
Erich Neumann	THE ORIGINS AND HISTORY OF CONSCIOUSNESS. *Vol. I,* TB/2007; *Vol. II,* TB/2008
St.-John Perse	SEAMARKS. Translated by Wallace Fowlie TB/2002
Jean Seznec	THE SURVIVAL OF THE PAGAN GODS: *The Mythological Tradition and Its Place in Renaissance Humanism and Art.* Illustrated TB/2004
Heinrich Zimmer	MYTHS AND SYMBOLS IN INDIAN ART AND CIVILIZATION TB/2005

HARPER TORCHBOOKS / The Academy Library

James Baird	ISHMAEL: *A Study of the Symbolic Mode in Primitivism* TB/1023
Herschel Baker	THE IMAGE OF MAN: *A Study of the Idea of Human Dignity in Classical Antiquity, the Middle Ages, and the Renaissance* TB/1047
Jacques Barzun	THE HOUSE OF INTELLECT TB/1051
W. J. Bate	FROM CLASSIC TO ROMANTIC: *Premises of Taste in Eighteenth Century England* TB/1036
Henri Bergson	TIME AND FREE WILL: *An Essay on the Immediate Data of Consciousness* TB/1021
H. J. Blackham	SIX EXISTENTIALIST THINKERS: *Kierkegaard, Jaspers, Nietzsche, Marcel, Heidegger, Sartre* TB/1002
Walter Bromberg	THE MIND OF MAN: *A History of Psychotherapy and Psychoanalysis* TB/1003
Abraham Cahan	THE RISE OF DAVID LEVINSKY. A novel. Introduction by John Higham TB/1028
Helen Cam	ENGLAND BEFORE ELIZABETH TB/1026
Joseph Charles	THE ORIGINS OF THE AMERICAN PARTY SYSTEM TB/1049
T. C. Cochran & William Miller	THE AGE OF ENTERPRISE: *A Social History of Industrial America* TB/1054
Norman Cohn	THE PURSUIT OF THE MILLENNIUM: *Revolutionary Messianism in Medieval and Reformation Europe and its Bearing on Modern Totalitarian Movements* TB/1037
G. G. Coulton	MEDIEVAL VILLAGE, MANOR, AND MONASTERY TB/1022
Wilfrid Desan	THE TRAGIC FINALE: *An Essay on the Philosophy of Jean-Paul Sartre* TB/1030
Cora Du Bois	THE PEOPLE OF ALOR: *A Social-Psychological Study of an East Indian Island. Vol. I,* 85 illus., TB/1042; *Vol. II,* TB/1043
George Eliot	DANIEL DERONDA. A novel. Introduction by F. R. Leavis TB/1039
John N. Figgis	POLITICAL THOUGHT FROM GERSON TO GROTIUS: 1414-1625: *Seven Studies.* Introduction by Garrett Mattingly TB/1032
Editors of *Fortune*	AMERICA IN THE SIXTIES: *The Economy and the Society* TB/1015
F. L. Ganshof	FEUDALISM TB/1058
G. P. Gooch	ENGLISH DEMOCRATIC IDEAS IN THE SEVENTEENTH CENTURY TB/1006
Francis J. Grund	ARISTOCRACY IN AMERICA: *A Study of Jacksonian Democracy* TB/1001
W. K. C. Guthrie	THE GREEK PHILOSOPHERS: *From Thales to Aristotle* TB/1008
Marcus Lee Hansen	THE ATLANTIC MIGRATION: 1607-1860 TB/1052
Alfred Harbage	AS THEY LIKED IT: *A Study of Shakespeare's Moral Artistry* TB/1035
J. M. Hussey	THE BYZANTINE WORLD TB/1057
Henry James	THE PRINCESS CASAMASSIMA. A novel. Intro. by Clinton Oliver. TB/1005
Henry James	RODERICK HUDSON. A novel. Introduction by Leon Edel TB/1016
Henry James	THE TRAGIC MUSE. A novel. Introduction by Leon Edel TB/1017
William James	PSYCHOLOGY: *The Briefer Course.* Edited with an Introduction by Gordon Allport TB/1034
Arnold Kettle	AN INTRODUCTION TO THE ENGLISH NOVEL. *Vol. I, Defoe to George Eliot,* TB/1011; *Vol. II, Henry James to the Present,* TB/1012
Samuel Noah Kramer	SUMERIAN MYTHOLOGY: *A Study of Spiritual and Literary Achievement in the Third Millennium B.C.* Illustrated TB/1055
Paul Oskar Kristeller	RENAISSANCE THOUGHT: *The Classic, Scholastic, and Humanist Strains* TB/1048
L. S. B. Leakey	ADAM'S ANCESTORS: *The Evolution of Man and His Culture.* Illustrated TB/1019
Bernard Lewis	THE ARABS IN HISTORY TB/1029
Ferdinand Lot	THE END OF THE ANCIENT WORLD AND THE BEGINNINGS OF THE MIDDLE AGES TB/1044

Arthur O. Lovejoy	THE GREAT CHAIN OF BEING: *A Study of the History of an Idea* TB/1009
Robert Lowie	PRIMITIVE SOCIETY. Introduction by Fred Eggan TB/1058
Niccolo Machiavelli	HISTORY OF FLORENCE AND OF THE AFFAIRS OF ITALY: *From the Earliest Times to the Death of Lorenzo the Magnificent.* Introduction by Felix Gilbert TB/1027
J. P. Mayer	ALEXIS DE TOCQUEVILLE: *A Biographical Study in Political Science* TB/1014
John U. Nef	CULTURAL FOUNDATIONS OF INDUSTRIAL CIVILIZATION TB/1024
Jose Oretga y Gasset	THE MODERN THEME. Introduction by Jose Ferrater Mora TB/1038
J. H. Parry	THE ESTABLISHMENT OF THE EUROPEAN HEGEMONY: 1415-1715: *Trade and Exploration in the Age of the Renaissance* TB/1045
Robert Payne	HUBRIS: *A Study of Pride.* Foreword by Herbert Read TB/1031
Samuel Pepys	THE DIARY OF SAMUEL PEPYS: Selections, edited by O. F. Morshead; illustrated by Ernest H. Shepard TB/1007
Paul E. Pfeutze	SELF, SOCIETY, EXISTENCE: *Human Nature and Dialogue in the Thought of George Herbert Mead and Martin Buber* TB/1059
Georges Poulet	STUDIES IN HUMAN TIME: *Montaigne, Molière, Baudelaire, Proust, et al.* TB/1004
George E. Probst, *Ed.*	THE HAPPY REPUBLIC: *A Reader in Tocqueville's America* TB/1060
Priscilla Robertson	REVOLUTIONS OF 1848: *A Social History* TB/1025
Ferdinand Schevill	THE MEDICI. Illustrated TB/1010
Bruno Snell	THE DISCOVERY OF THE MIND: *The Greek Origins of European Thought* TB/1018
C. P. Snow	TIME OF HOPE. A novel TB/1040
Perrin Stryker	THE CHARACTER OF THE EXECUTIVE: *Eleven Studies in Managerial Qualities* TB/1041
Percy Sykes	A HISTORY OF EXPLORATION. Introduction by John K. Wright TB/1046
Dorothy Van Ghent	THE ENGLISH NOVEL: *Form and Function* TB/1050
W. H. Walsh	PHILOSOPHY OF HISTORY: *An Introduction* TB/1020
W. Lloyd Warner	SOCIAL CLASS IN AMERICA: *The Evaluation of Status* TB/1013
Alfred N. Whitehead	PROCESS AND REALITY: *An Essay in Cosmology* TB/1033
Louis B. Wright	CULTURE ON THE MOVING FRONTIER TB/1053

HARPER TORCHBOOKS / The Science Library

Angus d'A. Bellairs	REPTILES: *Life History, Evolution, and Structure.* Illustrated TB/520
L. von Bertalanffy	PROBLEMS OF LIFE: *An Evaluation of Modern Biological and Scientific Thought* TB/521
David Bohm	CAUSALITY AND CHANCE IN MODERN PHYSICS. Foreword by Louis de Broglie TB/536
R. B. Braithwaite	SCIENTIFIC EXPLANATION TB/515
P. W. Bridgman	THE NATURE OF THERMODYNAMICS TB/537
Louis de Broglie	PHYSICS AND MICROPHYSICS. Foreword by Albert Einstein TB/514
J. Bronowski	SCIENCE AND HUMAN VALUES TB/505
A. J. Cain	ANIMAL SPECIES AND THEIR EVOLUTION. Illustrated TB/519
R. E. Coker	THIS GREAT AND WIDE SEA: *An Introduction to Oceanography and Marine Biology.* Illustrated TB/551
T. G. Cowling	MOLECULES IN MOTION: *An Introduction to the Kinetic Theory of Gases.* Illustrated TB/516
A. C. Crombie, *Ed.*	TURNING POINTS IN PHYSICS TB/535
W. C. Dampier, *Ed.*	READINGS IN THE LITERATURE OF SCIENCE. Illustrated TB/512
H. Davenport	THE HIGHER ARITHMETIC: *An Introduction to the Theory of Numbers* TB/526
W. H. Dowdeswell	ANIMAL ECOLOGY. Illustrated TB/543
W. H. Dowdeswell	THE MECHANISM OF EVOLUTION TB/527
C. V. Durell	READABLE RELATIVITY TB/530
Arthur Eddington	SPACE, TIME AND GRAVITATION: *An Outline of the General Relativity Theory* TB/510
Alexander Findlay	CHEMISTRY IN THE SERVICE OF MAN. Illustrated TB/524
H. G. Forder	GEOMETRY: *An Introduction.* Illus. TB/548
Gottlob Frege	THE FOUNDATIONS OF ARITHMETIC TB/534
R. W. Gerard	UNRESTING CELLS. Illustrated TB/541
Werner Heisenberg	PHYSICS AND PHILOSOPHY: *The Revolution in Modern Science* TB/549
C. Judson Herrick	THE EVOLUTION OF HUMAN NATURE TB/545
Max Jammer	CONCEPTS OF SPACE TB/533
Max Jammer	CONCEPTS OF FORCE TB/550
S. Korner	THE PHILOSOPHY OF MATHEMATICS: *An Introduction* TB/547
David Lack	DARWIN'S FINCHES: *The General Biological Theory of Evolution.* Illustrated TB/544

D. E. Littlewood	THE SKELETON KEY OF MATHEMATICS: *A Simple Account of Complex Algebraic Theories* TB/525
J. E. Morton	MOLLUSCS: *An Introduction to Their Form and Function*. Illustrated TB/529
O. Neugebauer	THE EXACT SCIENCES IN ANTIQUITY TB/552
J. R. Partington	A SHORT HISTORY OF CHEMISTRY. Illustrated TB/522
H. T. Pledge	SCIENCE SINCE 1500: *A Short History of Mathematics, Physics, Chemistry, and Biology*. Illustrated TB/506
John Read	A DIRECT ENTRY TO ORGANIC CHEMISTRY. Illustrated TB/523
O. W. Richards	THE SOCIAL INSECTS. Illustrated TB/542
George Sarton	ANCIENT SCIENCE AND MODERN CIVILIZATION TB/501
Paul A. Schilpp, *Ed.*	ALBERT EINSTEIN: *Philosopher-Scientist. Vol. I*, TB/502; *Vol. II*, TB/503
P. M. Sheppard	NATURAL SELECTION AND HEREDITY. Illustrated TB/528
Edmund W. Sinnott	CELL AND PSYCHE: *The Biology of Purpose* TB/546
L. S. Stebbing	A MODERN INTRODUCTION TO LOGIC TB/538
O. G. Sutton	MATHEMATICS IN ACTION. Foreword by James R. Newman. Illustrated TB/518
Stephen Toulmin	THE PHILOSOPHY OF SCIENCE: *An Introduction* TB/513
A. G. Van Melsen	FROM ATOMOS TO ATOM: *The History of the Concept* Atom TB/517
Friedrich Waismann	INTRODUCTION TO MATHEMATICAL THINKING. Foreword by Karl Menger TB/511
W. H. Watson	ON UNDERSTANDING PHYSICS: *An Analysis of the Philosophy of Physics.* Introduction by Ernest Nagel TB/507
G. J. Whitrow	THE STRUCTURE AND EVOLUTION OF THE UNIVERSE: *An Introduction to Cosmology*. Illustrated TB/504
Edmund Whittaker	HISTORY OF THE THEORIES OF AETHER AND ELECTRICITY. *Vol. I, The Classical Theories*, TB/531; *Vol. II, The Modern Theories*, TB/532
A. Wolf	A HISTORY OF SCIENCE, TECHNOLOGY, AND PHILOSOPHY IN THE SIXTEENTH AND SEVENTEENTH CENTURIES. Illustrated. *Vol. I*, TB/508; *Vol. II*, TB/509
A. Wolf	A HISTORY OF SCIENCE, TECHNOLOGY, AND PHILOSOPHY IN THE EIGHTEENTH CENTURY. *Vol. I*, TB/539; *Vol. II*, TB/540

HARPER TORCHBOOKS / The Cloister Library

Tor Andrae	MOHAMMED: *The Man and His Faith* TB/62
Augustine/Przywara	AN AUGUSTINE SYNTHESIS TB/35
Roland H. Bainton	THE TRAVAIL OF RELIGIOUS LIBERTY TB/30
C. K. Barrett, *Ed.*	THE NEW TESTAMENT BACKGROUND: *Selected Documents* TB/86
Karl Barth	DOGMATICS IN OUTLINE TB/56
Karl Barth	THE WORD OF GOD AND THE WORD OF MAN TB/13
Nicolas Berdyaev	THE BEGINNING AND THE END TB/14
Nicolas Berdyaev	THE DESTINY OF MAN TB/61
Anton T. Boisen	THE EXPLORATION OF THE INNER WORLD: *A Study of Mental Disorder and Religious Experience* TB/87
J. H. Breasted	DEVELOPMENT OF RELIGION AND THOUGHT IN ANCIENT EGYPT TB/57
Martin Buber	ECLIPSE OF GOD: *Studies in the Relation Between Religion and Philosophy* TB/12
Martin Buber	MOSES: *The Revelation and the Covenant* TB/27
Martin Buber	THE PROPHETIC FAITH TB/73
Martin Buber	TWO TYPES OF FAITH: *The interpenetration of Judaism and Christianity* TB/75
R. Bultmann, et al.	KERYGMA AND MYTH: *A Theological Debate*. Ed. by H. W. Bartsch TB/80
Jacob Burckhardt	THE CIVILIZATION OF THE RENAISSANCE IN ITALY. Illustrated Edition. Introduction by Benjamin Nelson and Charles Trinkaus. *Vol. I*, TB/40; *Vol. II*, TB/41
Emile Cailliet	PASCAL: *The Emergence of Genius* TB/82
Edward Conze	BUDDHISM: *Its Essence and Development* TB/58
Frederick Copleston	MEDIEVAL PHILOSOPHY TB/76
F. M. Cornford	FROM RELIGION TO PHILOSOPHY: *A Study in the Origins of Western Speculation* TB/20
G. G. Coulton	MEDIEVAL FAITH AND SYMBOLISM [Part I of "Art and the Reformation"]. Illustrated TB/25
G. G. Coulton	THE FATE OF MEDIEVAL ART IN THE RENAISSANCE AND REFORMATION [Part II of "Art and the Reformation"]. Illustrated TB/26
H. G. Creel	CONFUCIUS AND THE CHINESE WAY TB/63
Adolf Deissmann	PAUL: *A Study in Social and Religious History* TB/15
C. H. Dodd	THE AUTHORITY OF THE BIBLE TB/43
Johannes Eckhart	MEISTER ECKHART: A Modern Translation TB/8
Mircea Eliade	COSMOS AND HISTORY: *The Myth of the Eternal Return* TB/50

Mircea Eliade THE SACRED AND THE PROFANE: *The Significance of Religious Myth, Symbolism, and Ritual Within Life and Culture* TB/81

Morton S. Enslin CHRISTIAN BEGINNINGS TB/5

Morton S. Enslin THE LITERATURE OF THE CHRISTIAN MOVEMENT TB/6

G. P. Fedotov THE RUSSIAN RELIGIOUS MIND: *Kievan Christianity, the 10th to the 13th Centuries* TB/70

Ludwig Feuerbach THE ESSENCE OF CHRISTIANITY. Introduction by Karl Barth TB/11

Harry E. Fosdick A GUIDE TO UNDERSTANDING THE BIBLE TB/2

Henri Frankfort ANCIENT EGYPTIAN RELIGION: *An Interpretation* TB/77

Sigmund Freud ON CREATIVITY AND THE UNCONSCIOUS: *Papers on the Psychology of Art, Literature, Love, Religion.* Edited by Benjamin Nelson TB/45

Maurice Friedman MARTIN BUBER: *The Life of Dialogue* TB/64

O. B. Frothingham TRANSCENDENTALISM IN NEW ENGLAND: *A History* TB/59

Edward Gibbon THE TRIUMPH OF CHRISTENDOM IN THE ROMAN EMPIRE [J. B. Bury Edition, illus., Chapters 15-20 of "The Decline and Fall"] TB/46

C. C. Gillispie GENESIS AND GEOLOGY: *A Study in the Relations of Scientific Thought, Natural Theology, and Social Opinion in Great Britain, 1790-1850* TB/51

Maurice Goguel JESUS AND THE ORIGINS OF CHRISTIANITY I: *Prolegomena to the Life of Jesus* TB/65

Maurice Goguel JESUS AND THE ORIGINS OF CHRISTIANITY II: *The Life of Jesus* TB/66

Edgar J. Goodspeed A LIFE OF JESUS TB/1

H. J. C. Grierson CROSS-CURRENTS IN 17TH CENTURY ENGLISH LITERATURE: *The World, the Flesh, the Spirit* TB/47

William Haller THE RISE OF PURITANISM TB/22

Adolf Harnack WHAT IS CHRISTIANITY? Introduction by Rudolf Bultmann TB/17

R. K. Harrison THE DEAD SEA SCROLLS: *An Introduction* TB/84

Edwin Hatch THE INFLUENCE OF GREEK IDEAS ON CHRISTIANITY TB/18

Friedrich Hegel ON CHRISTIANITY: *Early Theological Writings* TB/79

Karl Heim CHRISTIAN FAITH AND NATURAL SCIENCE TB/16

F. H. Heinemann EXISTENTIALISM AND THE MODERN PREDICAMENT TB/28

S. R. Hopper, *Ed.* SPIRITUAL PROBLEMS IN CONTEMPORARY LITERATURE TB/21

Johan Huizinga ERASMUS AND THE AGE OF REFORMATION. Illustrated TB/19

Aldous Huxley THE DEVILS OF LOUDUN: *A Study in the Psychology of Power Politics and Mystical Religion in the France of Cardinal Richelieu* TB/60

Flavius Josephus THE GREAT ROMAN-JEWISH WAR, with *The Life of Josephus.* TB/74

Immanuel Kant RELIGION WITHIN THE LIMITS OF REASON ALONE. TB/67

Soren Kierkegaard EDIFYING DISCOURSES: A Selection TB/32

Soren Kierkegaard THE JOURNALS OF KIERKEGAARD: A Selection. Edited by A. Dru TB/52

Soren Kierkegaard PURITY OF HEART TB/4

Soren Kierkegaard THE POINT OF VIEW FOR MY WORK AS AN AUTHOR: *A Report to History* TB/88

Alexandre Koyré FROM THE CLOSED WORLD TO THE INFINITE UNIVERSE TB/31

Walter Lowrie KIERKEGAARD. *Vol I*, TB/89; *Vol. II*, TB/90

Emile Mâle THE GOTHIC IMAGE: *Religious Art in France of the 13th Century.* Illustrated TB/44

T. J. Meek HEBREW ORIGINS TB/69

H. Richard Niebuhr CHRIST AND CULTURE TB/3

H. Richard Niebuhr THE KINGDOM OF GOD IN AMERICA TB/49

Martin P. Nilsson GREEK FOLK RELIGION TB/78

H. J. Rose RELIGION IN GREECE AND ROME TB/55

Josiah Royce THE RELIGIOUS ASPECT OF PHILOSOPHY: *A Critique of the Bases of Conduct and Faith* TB/29

George Santayana INTERPRETATIONS OF POETRY AND RELIGION TB/9

George Santayana WINDS OF DOCTRINE *and* PLATONISM AND THE SPIRITUAL LIFE TB/24

F. Schleiermacher ON RELIGION: *Speeches to Its Cultured Despisers* TB/36

H. O. Taylor THE EMERGENCE OF CHRISTIAN CULTURE IN THE WEST: *The Classical Heritage of the Middle Ages* TB/48

P. Teilhard de Chardin THE PHENOMENON OF MAN TB/83

D. W. Thomas, *Ed.* DOCUMENTS FROM OLD TESTAMENT TIMES TB/85

Paul Tillich DYNAMICS OF FAITH TB/42

Ernst Troeltsch THE SOCIAL TEACHING OF THE CHRISTIAN CHURCHES. Introduction by H. Richard Niebuhr. *Vol. I*, TB/71; *Vol. II*, TB/72

E. B. Tylor THE ORIGINS OF CULTURE [Part I of "Primitive Culture"]. Introduction by Paul Radin TB/33

E. B. Tylor RELIGION IN PRIMITIVE CULTURE [Part II of "Primitive Culture"]. Introduction by Paul Radin TB/34

Evelyn Underhill WORSHIP TB/10

Johannes Weiss EARLIEST CHRISTIANITY: *A History of the Period* A.D. *30-150.* Introduction by F. C. Grant. *Vol. I*, TB/53; *Vol. II*, TB/54

Wilhelm Windelband A HISTORY OF PHILOSOPHY I: *Greek, Roman, Medieval* TB/38

Wilhelm Windelband A HISTORY OF PHILOSOPHY II: *Renaissance, Enlightenment, Modern* TB/39